'Lorna' by Anne Noble.
Photograph by Elizabeth Lightbody.

the female line

northern irish women writers

EDITED BY RUTH HOOLEY

**NORTHERN IRELAND
WOMEN'S RIGHTS MOVEMENT**

To celebrate the tenth anniversary
of the
Northern Ireland Women's Rights Movement

First published in 1985
by the Northern Ireland Women's Rights Movement
18 Lower Donegall Street, Belfast BT1 2GP
with the assistance of
the Equal Opportunities Commission for Northern Ireland
and the Arts Council of Northern Ireland.

Printed by the Universities Press.

British Library Cataloguing in Publication Data
The female line : Northern Irish women writers.
  1. English literature—Northern Irish authors
  2. English literature—Women authors
  3. English literature—20th century
  I. Hooley, Ruth   II. Northern Ireland Women's Rights Movement
  820.8'09287   PR8891.N6

ISBN 0-948599-00-6

Contents

Introduction

We are living in a decade which has seen the setting-up and expansion of women-only publishing houses throughout the world. 'A whole new commercial apparatus has come into being whereby more women writers are at last gaining recognition. Without the increasing demand for books by and about women the disproportionate silence would continue. The time is hopefully past when a male nom de plume was a pre-requisite for publication; or when an introduction by an eminent person was felt necessary to validate the work of a female author (e.g., Lord Dunsany's introduction to *Bridie Steen* by Anne Crone).

Here in Northern Ireland there is little evidence of any such evolution. Relatively few female authors find their way onto reading lists for higher and further education courses. Few female authors stare out from the covers of locally published fiction and poetry. (For instance, The Blackstaff Press's ratio of single-author poetry books is in the region of two female to fifteen male poets.) This silence is ambiguous. Does it mean an absence – there are hardly any women writing? Is it due to suppression – women lack confidence and opportunities to develop their writing? Is it a result of oppression – women are discriminated against in terms of what is taken seriously and which material matters? Or is it a passive resistance by those who find the language so steeped in gender-biased values as to be alien and inadequate to express their meaning?

In publishing this first collection of writings by Northern Irish women writers the Northern Ireland Women's Rights Movement is not putting forward a particular viewpoint or political slant. *The Female Line* is feminist in that the book is a women-only publication. However the contents express the many different voices of women in and from Northern Ireland, drawing on

1

their actual experience and creative imagination. This anthology is unusual in two ways: it includes both published and previously unpublished female authors side by side, writing in a wide range of forms and styles. The result is a miscellany of poetry, verse, short stories, reflections and extracts from novels and plays. The aim of the book is to highlight what is being written and to encourage more women towards publication. It is left to the reader to judge whether women write differently from men, are concerned with separate issues, or approach language differently.

As editor I have tried to select what is representative and of genuine interest. Finding the predominant themes to relate to family and personal life, the pieces are arranged in an informal sequence which moves through childhood, adolescence, growing awarenesses, personal relationships at various stages, marriage, motherhood, disillusionnment, independence and old age. Woven through these is another common theme, 'The Troubles' (these never being very far from the door).

With the concentration of focus on the home and family, it might have seemed appropriate to give this collection a title identifying women with their traditional role. But this would have ignored the emergence of women's lives beyond the limitations of the domestic situation. Themes of escape, of the imagination, and more particularly the birth of a self as an independent, political being are central to the developing literature of women writers. What emerges most readily from these writings are mixed feelings of dis-satisfaction, alienation, affection and humour: a sense of belonging and disowning. *The Female Line* is both handed-down and self-written. I hope that it will be read with this in mind.

Ruth Hooley.

The Chain

Anne Tannahill

It was very hot that day. When you crossed to the sunny side of the street, it was like coming out of the dark picture-house into daylight. But even on the shady side it was warm enough to make your hands sticky and slippy. Because of this we had given up playing three-ball against the wall of Jean's house and were going to play shops instead. Jean had a toy cash-register and both of us had been collecting empty packets and tins for months.

When I went into the house to get my stuff, I was almost blinded for a moment with the after-images from the street shifting and dazzling in front of my eyes. My mother called me from the kitchen where she was ironing and said I could put on my bathing-costume if I wanted. Usually she would not let me wear it unless we were at the seaside, even when half the kids in the street were out in only their shorts or knickers.

She was going to have a baby again and she was very fat. I liked it when she was expecting because, although she was crosser than usual, she had a constant craving for ice lollies. She would send me round to the sweetie shop two or three times a day and always say, 'Get one for yourself.' This day, I had been round three times already and when I came back into the kitchen after putting my bathing-costume on, she gave me money to go again. Before I went she tied my plaits up in a ribbon on top of my head. 'That'll keep you cooler,' she said.

I got her two lollies and one each for Jean and me and then I brought out my cardboard box of shop things and the wooden stool for a counter. We hunkered down and set out all the stuff very carefully. This was the best part of playing shops. The buying and selling bit was usually spoiled because we fought about who would be the shop lady first. So we made the fixing up last as long as possible. We made neat piles of cigarette packets and matchboxes and tobacco tins on the stool beside the cash-register. On the window-sill behind the stool we put the bigger things – packets of soap powder and cornflakes.

While we were arranging the bigger packets, a man came walking up the street from the main road and stopped to watch us. Both of us started to show off a bit, trying to make our voices sound English and watching him out of the corners of our eyes. After a while he sat down on the pavement near us, with his back against the wall and his knees drawn up almost touching his chest. We went on showing off and letting on not to see him.

Then he began to whistle a tune softly under his breath. He was good at whistling. We stopped playing and listened to him, gradually forgetting the pretence and looking openly at him. He looked young, younger than my father, and very clean and tanned. His clothes were like Sunday clothes, dark trousers and white shirt, but he had no tie or jacket on and his sleeves were rolled up. He was fair-haired and against his brown skin his hair and moustache and even his eyelashes looked white. He was playing with a fine gold chain, letting it trickle like yellow water from one hand to another. We watched, fascinated. Now he was pretending not to see us, but I saw him twice glance swiftly at us, although he kept his head bowed over the chain. His arms were covered in tatoos of snakes and birds and hearts. My uncle had tatoos like that, that he had got in the Navy during the war.

Watching the chain, I said, 'Were you in the Navy, Mister?' The whistling ceased. He stopped spilling the chain from hand to hand and lifted his head and looked at me as if he did not understand me. 'During the war. Were you in the Navy?'

He kept on looking at me. Then he glanced at Jean and lowered his head. The chain began to shimmer and fall between his hands again. 'Yes. Yes, I was.'

'Well, were you ever in Hong Kong?' My uncle had told me about Hong Kong, but long before that I had been fascinated by the sound of the place, saying it over

4

and over to myself. I thought vaguely that the King Kong that we had seen at a Saturday matinee must come from there. The man lifted his head and looked at me again. 'Yes, I was in Hong Kong.'

'Did you like it? My Uncle Alec didn't like it.' He remained silent. It was hard to believe that the chain was not some sort of liquid pouring like a waterfall into the pool of his cupped hand.

'Did you get that chain in Hong Kong, Mister?' It was Jean who asked the question. She did not like me getting all the attention.

This time it was even longer before he answered. When he did, he kept his head down. 'No, I got it near here. There's a whole pile of them. I just picked one up. They don't belong to anybody. They're on a bomb site.'

We were silent, impressed. People did find things in the ruins. One of my father's mates had picked up a scorched snuff-box from a pile of rubble and found a fiver in it. The big piece of white paper had been folded and folded until it fitted the box. All the people in the house had been killed in the Blitz, so my father's mate just kept the money. After that, a lot of the bigger boys had spent three or four days just digging about in the rubble and dust. Where we lived was near the docks, and an awful lot of the streets near us had been flattened.

But the boys never found anything much, and one of them got his hand all crushed when part of a wall fell on him. Even before that happened, my mother had forbidden us to go near the ruins. Drunk men used them for toilets on Saturday nights and anyway there were rats in them. 'Hiving with rats,' my mother had said. 'As big as cats.' I had sat and stared at our old tabby for a long time, trying to imagine a rat that size.

'Do you want to come and I'll show you where they are?' the man asked. We hesitated.

'We're not allowed,' Jean began. I thought of the chains all lying there in the dust. The image was linked in my mind with a picture I had seen somewhere of Aladdin running his hands through jewels and silks that were spilling out of a wooden chest.

'Where are they?' I said.

'Come on,' the man said. He stood up and started to walk down the street. We followed, not looking at each other. He turned the corner and walked past the shops on the main road and round the corner again up into the next street. He was going very fast and we had to half-run to keep up with him. Without looking back at us, he turned down the entry that ran down the side of the first house. When we caught up with him, he was standing beside the back wall of one of the shops that had been bombed.

'They're in here,' he said. He did not look at us. I felt funny. I did not really want to go now. There was a baker's and a butcher's in that row of shops, and my mother had said that that was where the rats were the biggest and the fattest in the district. Besides, it was dank and smelly in the entry. I shivered, and felt the goose pimples come up on my bare arms and legs. I looked at Jean, but she would not look at me. I tried to think of an excuse to get back to the sunny street. Then I realised that the only way to get into the ruins was through an opening that had been a window once.

'That's too high for us to get in,' I said, trying not to sound relieved.

The man looked up at the opening. 'I'll help you in,' he said. I swallowed. My throat felt tight and strange, and suddenly I needed to go to the toilet. I looked at Jean again. She was kicking her foot against the bottom of the wall, frowning down at it.

'You go in and get them for us, Mister,' I said. Jean stopped kicking. The man looked quickly at me and looked away again. He did not say anything for what seemed like a long time. Jean began to kick again.

'It doesn't matter then,' he said at last, and started to walk back to the street. I thought of all the chains.

'All right,' I said. 'You can help us in.'

He came back again. 'You first,' he said to Jean, and lifted her by the waist so that she could get one leg over the window sill. She looked into the ruins and then back over her shoulder at me.

6

It's all right,' she said. 'You don't have to jump down or anything. There's a big pile of stones to climb down on.' She threw her other leg over and started to clamber down.

'Now you,' the man said. His voice sounded hoarse, as if he had a cold. I shivered again as he lifted me on to the sill. As I started to go down to where Jean was, the man put his hands on the sill and sprang up, turning so that he landed in a sitting position. Turning again to face me, he started to crawl through the opening, keeping low so that he would not bump his head. Suddenly he stopped.

There was a noise in the entry. I could hear women talking in excited voices and a man shouting, 'I'll swing for him! I'll bloody swing for him!' A stone moved under my foot and I almost fell. When I got my balance back, I looked up and the man was gone. I could hear him running down the entry, then women screaming and the other man swearing, and then the sound of running feet again. 'Don't worry, I'll get the bugger!' the voice shouted, and I heard somebody else run out of the entry. I was shivering so much that the stones were shifting beneath me as I tried to reach the sill again. Behind me, I could hear Jean starting to cry.

Next day, it was hot again and we were setting out all the stuff for the shop. Neither of us had said anything about the man. Jean frowned at a bashed cigarette packet she was trying to force back into shape again. 'What do you think he was going to do?' she asked suddenly.

I jabbed at the keys on the cash-register. 'I think he was going to kill us,' I said. I had thought about it a lot since our mothers had taken us down to the police station and the lady had asked us all the questions. I had been thinking about it when my father had come home from work. My mother had called him into the scullery and they had talked for a long time. I had not been able to make out what they said, but my father had started to sound angry, and my mother had begun to cry again.

'Yes, he was going to kill us,' I said.

7

Jean gave up trying to fix the packet and put it at the bottom of the pile where it would not show. 'Was he going to stab us with a knife?' she asked.

I thought a minute. 'No. I worked it all out last night after I went to bed. He was going to strangle us.'

Jean stared at me. 'How do you know that?'

'Easy,' I said. 'That's what the chain was for.'

Her face cleared. 'That's right,' she said. 'That's what the chain was for.'

Indefinite Article

Francine Cunningham

A child
grows to find
a world
nowhere near
as assured
as the one
it has left

a dictionary
replaces
The Word
on my book shelf.

The Dolls

Laura Shier

We stayed at O'Hallihan's select boarding-house.
The girls had a room with flower-striped paper.
Along the shore we bathed our dolls in pools,
Where green seaweed fingered out from the rocks,
Our plump forearms angling as they broke the surface.
Sharp crustaceans nipped at our knees as we knelt.
How smooth and firm the waxen feel
Of the little bodies of our lovely children!

But the salt sea-water rotted the bands
That threaded their limbs, so their arms
And legs fell off. We cried, and then
We gave the dolls to the children who came
To beg at the kitchen for dripping.
They wore no shoes or socks. They were poor.
Perhaps they did not mind that their children
Had no legs or arms. They had no other dolls.

A Child Falling from a Cliff
Laura Shier

People would come, in cars, to stand on the ciff
And gaze down, timorous, wondering if
A child could really fall to the rocky shore
And take no serious harm. I wore
A heavy plaster weighing on my arm,
And a white 'soldier's bandage' round my head.
'Will she be alright?' the people said.

And on the day
When I was to act in the play
My friend played my part
Wearing my costumes. With a sore heart
I sat and watched.
'It was a miracle,' the other parents said.
But I wondered if something was broken inside my head.

Knock Three Times
Stella Mahon

'You *can* get them.' Rough-voiced, age-old nine years spoke with the wisdom of one long-practised in his business.

'No I can't.'

'Look, all you do is wait till one comes, then you aim your stone a bit in front of it.' He demonstrated his skill with an easy but careful aim and a hit.

'Oh! It'll be hurt.'

'Naw.' A drawled denial. 'Can't hurt them,' he maintained. 'How could you hurt *them*? They're horrible. You can't hurt horrible things.'

She tried again to follow the instructions of her better. For, yes, he was that. Anyone who could so easily throw a stone from a high bridge and every time hit the rat he was aiming for, was undoubtedly the possessor of all those skills which made superiority. She failed. Her stone slapped into the mud at the side of the river, which the low tide always laid bare. It sank in, its own weight and the thrust of the throw oozing it slowly beneath the mud's surface. Like the lips of some large and slimy animal, the mud ingested her missile. There remained for a time a faint echo of her intrusion, but levels were found, smoothness returned.

'Too far that time,' he pronounced. 'You threw it too far. Look down thonder. There's another one. You can just about see it.' He was pointing straight down. She looked where she was told to look. Every so often she caught a glimpse of a rat tail, then a head, a tail, a head. It was going about some circular business only its small brain knew the point of.

'Wait,' he ordered. 'It'll come right out in a minute. Ach, that stone you've got's not big enough.' He produced a larger one after burrowing in his pocket. 'Here. You go again. I'll tell you when to throw.'

They waited, balanced on their bellies on the

bridge's stone parapet. She wriggled herself forward a bit, the better to see the prey. Her balance shifted, causing her heart to lurch along with her body. But she steadied herself. How awful to fall in. The thought made her shudder. She closed her eyes to shut out the sight of the mud which had almost threatened to welcome her. But she only succeeded in concentrating on her imagination's eye, the slow-motion of herself falling. She saw herself lying there, being drawn under, covered, all trace of her slowly removed. Away. No more.

It would go into me everywhere. Over me and into me.

'Throw!' The urgent shout broke her waking nightmare. She focussed her outer eyes on the skittering rat and fired her stone. It splatted into the mud about six inches directly in front of the rat's nose, the sound and movement pulling the animal up short. It turned a few confused circles, stopped again to twitch at the air with its snout. Then it darted for the safety of a piece of old drainpipe which lay in the long grass at the bottom of the river bank.

'Useless!' Exasperation and not a small amount of despising was in the half-whispered depreciative. Another rat scurried out from under the bridge. A stone flew out and caught it in the neck. It squealed sharply.

'Ach, you hurt it.' She looked across at him, anxiety markng her face.

'No I didn't. I told you, you can't hurt them.'

'Why did it squeal then?'

'It didn't squeal. It just squeaked a bit.'

'Then you must have hurt it.'

'Ach, you're stupid. What do you know?' He slid off the parapet and looked up at her. 'Anyway, I think you're too scared to even try to hit them. Just all stupid sissy about hurting them. Hurt rats! Huh!' He delivered his insults with a sneer in his voice and on his face, with all the assurance of the unsissified. He walked, hands-pocketed away, each step pushing her, her stupidity and her general handlessness into that part of his mind reserved for the unimportant.

12

She lay straddled across the parapet. He's off again. Just like that time I couldn't make the stone skim across the pond in the park. How many jumps did he get? Four, or was it five? Mine just plopped into the water. She stared at the mud. And watched the rats. They seemed to sense that the danger was gone. The head peering at them was no threat.

Somehow she caught their defiance of her. It challenged her. Indeed, his taunts had challenged her. I'll get a stone. I'll do it okay. She slid off the concrete parapet, rasping her knees and thighs as the roughness of the stone made her cotton dress ride up to the top of her knickers, then higher. Her belly felt the stone before the momentum of her slide planted her flat-footed on the pavement. She walked to the end of the bridge and onto the waste ground behind the row of houses which made up one side of her street. Her eyes scoured the tufted grass for a weapon of war. A big stone. Well, perhaps not too big. She picked up a piece of broken brick and weighed it in her hand as though she were an expert in assessing the worth of such items. It would do, she judged, and hurried back to the bridge. She mounted the parapet in an awkward clamber. There they were, still skittering about, three of them now. She selected her target. The big fat one. But it was heading back towards the bridge and reached the arch before she had a chance to take aim. I'll wait for him. He'll soon come back out again. Not thirty seconds passed before the large rat darted out into view again and nipped its way along the mud. She bit on her tongue for concentration, raised her arm and threw. The squeal, short as it was, told her that she had made a hit.

No thought that the squeal from her rat meant pain. Elation was too great for that. I did it! I hit the big rat! She wasted no time sliding from her perch in her former cautious manner, but flung herself onto the pavement and ran to the corner of the street. Two boys were playing marbles, one of them her erstwhile tutor, redundant in that capacity, now that she had met with success.

13

'I hit one,' she called out to him. 'I hit a rat.'

He glanced up from his game to stare at her in disbelief. The triumph on her face caused his expression to change momentarily to one of surprise, but disbelief won, returning as his considered reaction to her news.

'You're only saying that.'

'I'm not,' she retorted peevishly. 'One ran out from under the bridge and I hit it. With a piece of brick,' she added.

'Where?' he demanded.

'I don't know,' she confessed, suddenly doubting herself. She remembered the squeal. 'It cried,' she called out. 'The rat cried. I heard it. So I must have hit it.'

'Rats don't cry! You're a fibber.' He returned to his game. 'She's a fibber,' he repeated in emphasis to his opponent, as he expertly flicked his marble from the crook of his forefinger with his thumbnail. The other boy responded with a nod of agreement, lurching round on his haunches to take his shot. It was a movement which shut her out of their sphere.

She turned away slowly to go back to the bridge. I'm not fibbing. I did hit it. It cried. I heard it. It cried. Pain. She ran the rest of the way.

On the mud, the rat lay quite still, settled where it was by its own weight on the oily black softness. Her heart raced, pounded, when she saw it. No screamed itself inside her. I didn't mean to. It ran about after I hit it. I saw it. Get up rat. Get UP. No movement. The water of a tear filled each eye. She blinked to clear her sight. Get up. Please get up. Nothing. Again tears grew. To wipe these away she needed the back of a hand. She couldn't stay, couldn't keep on looking. She ran across the road to the far end of the bridge. A path there led from the river, through some wild ground, a short cut to a nearby street. Even though the thought of what she had done to the rat had forced her legs into movement, to carry her away, the horror of her act was not strong enough to stop her mind from pulling her body up short at the entrance to the path. Much as she wanted,

14

needed, to go down to it, she could move no further.

Her hidey-hole was there, down the path, across the long wild grass, hidden in the bushes, watched over by the straggly-branched trees. A secret place, to which she had only ever invited one other person. Her place of being alone, except for that one time when she and Emily had crept in to enjoy a secret shared.

She groaned. Oh, it was only a dream, part of her insisted. A fleeting reassurance allowed her to take a short step onto the path. You only dreamt the Scrunchy Man down there. He's not for real. Another hesitant step. Anyway, it's not dark down there now. It's daytime. Dreams are night-time things.

But night-time things have a living all of their own. And her dream had been so alive, had come so often, that it had in the end robbed her of her place, had taken away secret safety and given her secret fear.

Death-horror behind her, dream-fear before, she could not move on. Could not will herself to take possession of sanctuary.

It was not far off dusking by the time she reached her goal. Sentimental journey – is this what it's like? How could you be sentimental about this place? She looked around her. God, how it's changed. At least on the outside. The houses of the street that had been hers did not look quite so run-down as they had then. All those new extensions built on at the back, their new brick jarring with the old. No more arse-freezing sessions in the outside privy in the winter, or earwig watching in the summer, just the brightly-lit warmth of hygienic modernity. All the time in the world to be constipated, without the threat of frostbite in your vitals. She laughed to herself.

And the river. What have they *done* to it? To her knowledge, it had ever been tame, as flowing water goes. Almost but not quite stagnant in its murkiness, and correspondingly smelly. Those hot nights of high summer, when you either suffocated with the heat, or opened the window looking for a touch of air in motion – only to find the stench of the river replacing the little air you had, your breathing space diminished by river gas. It certainly wasn't what you would have called a babbling brook, not our river. Just bubbling, as the stinking fumes cauldroned their way to the surface.

A tame river. But not so the banks. They hadn't been tamed then, not destroyed as the river had been. They were grassy, untidily grassy, still belonging to nature. There were bushes and dandelions, the occasional buttercups and clumps of clover. A bit of wildness. And now look what they've done. She was lost at the sight of the concrete sides they had put on the river. More so than the changes she had seen in the houses, this violation done to the riverbanks had stolen her orientation, her sense of place in this townscape. She looked across to her right. Look at that, even the Black Pad's gone. Tarmac. Boring mechanical tarmac. The Pad, the way to the park, had been like a nature trail, growth tramped out of the pathway itself by thousands of pairs of feet. But the grassy, tangly borders, they had been alive.

Her gaze went back to the river. It's a sewer. They've cut the hypocrisy of years and finally turned it into what it has always been. But then we could still pretend – because we had the banks. In spite of the smell and the murkiness, we could believe the stories grannies told of people hiring boats out on it, swimming in it. In spite of the smell and the rats.

The rats. That big fat one. She saw again that whole summer afternoon flicking through her memory like a series of still photographs. Why on earth did I not go and tell those wee buggers to come and see the dead beastie? They'd have believed me then. A rueful smile crossed her face. Ach, they'd have still said I was fibbing. They'd have said it must just have dropped dead and told me to stop trying it on.

But as she remembered how she had felt that day – guilt, fear and a soul-aching sad emptiness – she knê the real reason why she did not fetch them. It wasn't trophy. Certainly not that. I tried for acceptance on their terms and got more than I bargained for. And what I got wasn't me. Sold my soul and killed a rat – the rhythm amused her – sold my soul and killed a rat, just to get my back a pat. Killed a rat and sold my soul, couldn't reach my hidey-hole.

Aaah! That! There was the place. Own space, me defined by it. Forced out of it, defined by someone else's space ever since. Oh, that's heavy stuff. But it couldn't be else. Not when I've just spent the last nine years with the rat boy, still trying to learn his games. Oh, not *him*. She contradicted herself, as though her thoughts had an audience. Not the marble king, stone skimmer without peer, but him disguised as someone else. Matrimonial marbles, skimming the stones of wedded bliss across life's unruffled pond.

She giggled to herself. Getting close to purple prose, here. She shivered. The sky had grown darker and a summer chill had taken possession of the air. Best go. What's that wee verse? 'She stood on the bridge at midnight, a thought suddenly entered her head. Why on earth am I standing here dreaming, when I should be home in bed?' And getting up in the morning to do all the things I'm supposed to do – and studiously avoid all the things I'm not supposed to do or think or be. At any rate keep them well enough hidden. Rat boy to rat girl – You wanna play in my yard? You gotta knock three times and give the magic passwords: I do, I will, I plight me. Rat girl to rat boy – Okay. There's nowhere much else to go anyway. But what about you? Don't you have to knock and give the passwords too? Naw. Sure I'm in the yard already. But if it keeps you happy...

She turned and crossed the road. And won't they all want to know where I've been. One, two, three, all together now: down *there*? What on earth took you back there? Do I have an answer? Not one that'll satisfy your man, at any rate. What was it he said that disgruntled day when he pointed out how lucky I didn't know I was? Fortunate to get away from there. If it hadn't been for him – oh, how did I keep a straight face? – I'd never have had the chance of travel, of living abroad. Of meeting all the kinds of interesting people he knew. Never have had a *nice* house, a colour TV, a car. I kept a straight face because it wasn't funny. He believed it. Couldn't imagine that I'd ever be so ungrateful as to want it any different. There's wanting and doing, though. If he took me away from here into his space, there's only one person can take me off into my own. Hasn't it been a bargain, though? Self sold for a colour TV. You're scared, she told herself. Too scared to take a step into your own yard. God, do you even have a yard to step into?

A few more steps brought her to the path that had led to her secret place. She stopped at its entrance. Is it still there? Or have they manhandled it into dead concrete too, just like the riverbanks? The path at least looked untouched, as untreated as it had ever been. She took a step onto it. Her breathing became heavy. The bushes were shadowy, the grass longer than she ever remembered it. Aw, come on now! You're a big girl these days. So it's nearly dark. So your sleep gave you a sickener of this place. But it *was* special. You can't not take a look. Hell, about the only time you ever had your own space was when you used to dive round here and enjoy it. That was before the Scrunchy Man, a little girl's voice said, deep inside her. A dream, said the woman in her to the child in her. Only a dream.

She began to walk along the path. Even in the shadows of approaching night, she could tell that it had not been touched at all. Not the path, not the grass, not the bushes. Her place would still be there too. She knew that just as surely as she knew that she was being followed. Rustling footfalls in the long grass. Breathing. She stopped, held her breath. It was not her own footfalls that she heard, that panting was not coming from her.

She felt that she had taken root. It was the dream come real. It was happening. Each time that misery had come to her in sleep, paid a return visit, she had known exactly what was going to happen, what she was going to

18

do, what *he* was going to do. Just as then, she knew now, step by step, what was to come, was trapped in it, no choice but to act her part. Legs weighted with fear she would walk to the end of the path, willing each foot forward, breathing terror into and out of herself, because of the breathing she was hearing behind her. With total resignation, she gave herself up to the inevitable. Move, legs, move.

She knew that by the time she reached the end of the path, he would be within arm's reach of her, but would bide his time. On, go on. Get away, even though you know you can't. The end of the path. She felt him behind her as she stepped out into the street, a street full of safe-looking houses. Felt him there, as she had always felt him in the dream. Now, inexplicably, she would turn to face him. Don't. Don't turn round! But that had been part of the dream too. Always she had said to herself: don't turn. But always, no exceptions, she had turned. She felt her body twisting now for the confrontation. No, she screamed inwardly. I don't want to see your scrunched-up face full of wrinkles, your leering eyes, your mouth that grins wetly at me. I won't look at your threadbare suit of wrinkle upon fold, upon wrinkle, see your hand with its brown-stained finger point at me, choose me, reach for me. Not this time.

She ran. Her effort of will over, she ran towards the houses, looking for one with lights behind the curtains. Even as she did so she was more than aware that this too was part of the act. The running had been part of the dream too, the search for a safe place. But she couldn't stop herself, couldn't will herself again into breaking the pattern, even though she knew the horror to come. She ran, looking in at each window for light. There. She approached the door. No, she tried to command herself. Not this too. Don't knock at the door. You know he'll be there. He'll be behind you, but it'll be him that opens the door in front of you. He'll open it, grinning at you, grinning yellow-teethed at you and your terror. Don't knock! But her hand was already reaching out, as though by some outside power. She closed her eyes and thought

19

her whole will into her outstretched arm. Pull it back, she commanded herself. But control was not there. All right you bastard, she hissed. I'll knock. And knock and knock. Her will grew suddenly strong, stronger than her fear. As she knocked, she looked behind her to spit her 'bastard' in his behind-her face, just as she would in the face that would appear before her. Noises in the hall. But she hardly heard them. She was staring at an empty street.

The door opened. 'Yes?' a soft voice questioned. She turned round to meet it. An ordinary voice, from ordinary lips in an ordinary woman's face.

They gave her a lift, because she had stood trembling on their doorstep. Fear, they thought. Poor thing! But by the time they reached the place where her bed for the night was, she knew it had not been all fear. It had been relief. And more than that, it had been release. Knocking at their door, she had knocked at her own, and found, in truth, that no one was barring her way. She could walk in.

Dreams

Una Woods

I strove to cut the old house free
Uncling its ivy from my memory walls
There was no way forward
But would short cut back
And place me half-size in the orchard

Cheating time's maturing power
The young apples snapped back, fought tight
I won, sliced with white teeth
Triumphant as the crows clamouring noise
Fidgeting around their raw sparse homes

An ancient farmer foraging in tractor tracks
Cut glib wisdom with his toothless spit
Begod them's high
High as your dreams child
Old grounded crow cackling in my ear still

Legacy

Ann W. Gleave

Just look there.
The cards foretold
that I should stare into the night
that I should harvest the moon cloud
that I should prey
should walk unseen
among my numbered stones.
I try to hide, unbidden,
in the ancient dark,
yet light finds me out
and I reel
as candles burn, down,
in time.
My legacy is to be spun out
of a steady course
to be unearthed,
stripped of all reason,
unable to say goodnight
but to whisper
Here's rosemary, that's for remembrance.
Here's a moon for all night
here's all I have
as the days gather on.
I hear not a word
for doors close quietly, down,
and it rains in whispers.

Pictures

Geraldine Bradley

The Pope and Kennedy merited esteem,
Pals upon the mantlepiece beside the china dogs.
And suckling deep on the chimney breast
The red-light heart of Jesus Christ
Summoned scarlet pictures in us all.
Blood-bead breaks on sallow brow
Jaundiced dew-eyes hissing holiness.
Not even behind the sofa crouching lower,
Could I evade the hammering screams,
Scourging cries.

Nursery Rhyme

Ruth Hooley

M is for Mummy
And man that I saw
Out through the window
Bare toes on the floor.

The man in the moon
Winked back when I waved
But mummy came in
And shushed him away.

She curtained the window
And tucked me in bed
But I hear him tapping
Inside my head.

M is for mummy
And man that I saw
Out through the window
Bare toes on the floor.

The Last Thing

Frances Molloy

That was the last thing a thought. A never thought he
could view it like that. It wasn't my fault. There was not a
thing a could have done. What would you have done, tell
me that? What could anybody have done? A was very
young at the time as ye know, but throughout it all, that
was the last thing a thought.

He went away to England to work for a year, to save
up for us to get married, ye see, and a was well-pleased
with meself when this good job came along for me,
looking after these three wains whose Mother was dead.
The father was a businessman that had done well for
himself. A mine feeling sorry for him the first time a met
him, thinking what a pity it was, him being left to bring
up three wains on his own and him old enough to be their
granda.

Since my wife died three months ago, he said to me
at the interview, a'v had problems with Joan. The doctor
says that it's the shock of her Mother's death, and she'll
get over it, but it's a worry all the same. Ye see, says he,
she hardly ever speaks to a soul now. She never plays
with any of her friends and she'll do no work for the
teacher at the school.

Me heart went out to her right away the minute a set
eyes on her. She had these big dark sad looking brown
eyes, and golden curls, beautiful they were, hanging
right down to her shoulders. She had the loveliest wee
face ye could see, pretty as anything, and a cute wee
dimple right in the middle of her chin. Ach, sure a'll
never forget her, the poor wee craythure, and her only
eight year old at the time.

A told him that a could start right away so he took
me to show me the house. It was big. Seven rooms
upstairs and it set in its own grounds. He kept a gardener
full time – an old grizzly grey fellow with a stumpy

25

temper. It didn't strike me as strange at the time, that he was paying nearly twice the usual wage for that kind of work. A was only too glad of it with me saving up to get married and him away in England doing the same.

A was given the best room in the house, nice and quiet, with a big window looking out over the front lawn. A suppose he must of slept there himself before the wife died. A was me own boss and a didn't have a lot to do. A woman come in for two hours every morning and she done the bulk of the cleaning and cooked the dinner. All a had to do was make the breakfast and the tay in the evening and get the wains out to school. But sure it was nothing, working in a house like that with all them mod-cons.

Most of me time a spent with wee Joan, playing with her and reading her wee stories to try and take her out of herself. A used to go down to the school at lunchtime to see if she was alright – and god, the way her wee face used to light up when she seen me coming, it would have done yer heart good. People started saying what a quare change they seen in her since a come. Her teacher even come out one day and shook hands with me and said a was a godsend, a real godsend.

A was there for about three months when a found out that things were not what they seemed. A took the flu as it happened and a had to get up in the middle of the night, a thing a didn't ususally do. In them days a was a good sleeper. It was two o'clock in the morning, a can still mine well looking at the luminous face of the alarm-clock when a woke up in a cold sweat. The bathroom was at the back of the house where the family slept and as a made me way towards it, silently, so as not to disturb anybody at that unearthly hour, a thought a heard a sob. Sound, as ye know, has an unnatural way of carrying in the stillness of the night, so a took two aspirin and a long drink of water and thought no more about it.

A was well up the landing near me own bedroom door when a heard the sound again. It was clearer this time, a sob and a muffled kind of a cry. Something was the matter with Joan. A ran straight to her room and as a opened her door and groped about for her light switch a

26

called out to reassure her, it's alright me love, a said, you're only having a nasty old dream.

Me first impression on entering the room was that he had heard her too and had got to her first. That impression didn't last long. He was bending over her wee naked body holding her thighs apart with his hands and his pyjamas were lying in an untidy lump on top of her favourite doll.

The second a seen what he was doing a screamed and run over to save her but a can't right mine what happened next. A must have fainted with the shock and the flu a suppose. The next thing a remember after that was being back in me bed with him sitting there beside me. He had his pyjamas back on again. The flu a had turned into pleurisy and me temperature went up wile high. For a wheen of days a thought a was going to die but he wouldn't get the doctor for me. Instead, he took a week off work to take care of me himself – imagine. A thought at the time that it was some kind of a horrible nightmare and a would wake up, but a didn't as ye know, it was only too real. He wouldn't even let the woman that done the cleaning into me room. He kept coming in himself and sitting on the side of me bed and me lying there hardly able to breathe.

He kept on saying, ye won't tell, now will ye, promise me that ye won't tell. A knew that he was mad so a had to promise just to humour him. A knew too that with him away in England, nobody was likely to miss me. A was very much at his mercy so a just had to lie there listening.

A'm a lonely a man, a lonely man, a very lonely man, he kept on saying over and over again. A wouldn't hurt her, a wouldn't hurt her for the world. She's me own, me very own wee girl.

After a wheen of days like this he started to hold me hand when he was talking. A was too feared at this stage, as you can surely understand, to do anything about it. He had the strangest glazed look in his eyes, then he started to poke at me. His affair went all hard and he started to jab it into me. A began to scream, a thought it

27

would kill me, than a passed out with the pain. When a come to he was still doing it. He had a wile look in his eyes and the slevers were dripping out of his mouth onto me face. The pain was so bad a could hardly stand it. A started to pray wile hard to Our Lady to save me. He kept doing it every day till a was near demented. A often think that if it hadn't been for the prayers a would have gone clean mad.

It was eight days after he first done it to me that a finally managed to escape. Somebody called at the house to see him and he forgot to lock me door. Thank god a had enough of me strength left to get up and be gone before he got back. It's amazing how quick ye can recover when ye'r young. A had me wheen of wee pounds tucked away safe in underneath me mattress and just enough time to get them out, but no time to pack me things. A was in a terrible state thinking about poor wee Joan. A hardly knew what to do for her so a went right away to the Redemptorists in the Antrim Road. They're very powerful men ye know, the Redemptorists, a've always had great faith in them.

The priest a talked to was very nice, indeed he couldn't have been nicer, and he was more than understanding when a went to confession. He said there was no way any blame could be attached to me, a was completely innocent of any sin. He said that a was very close to god and he made me promise in the confessional that a would never go near that man's house again. Of course a promised but a told him that a was wile worried about wee Joan. He asked me would a talk to him outside confession about that and a said a would. He took her name and address and said he would see that wee Joan was alright and he told me to pray for the man because he was evil. Indeed a still pray for him even though he's bound to be dead now for that was a long time ago.

Well, to make a long story short, a might as well tell ye, it kept playing on me mind. A had nobody to talk to with me Mother and father both dead, so a kept brooding about it in me head and worrying what had become of poor wee Joan.

A know now that a should not have told him about it when he came home from England at the christmas, but as a say, it kept playing on me mind and a needed somebody to talk to. The priest said a was still a virgin in the eyes of god and his church, but when a told him what happened, he said that he didn't want to marry a woman who wasn't pure.

Ye know, a thought a could depend on him. After all a had been through, a never thought that he could view it like that. That was the last thing a thought.

Rape

Christine Hammond

Bizarre, this new lexicon
sliding from the lips of the law,
confusing provocation
and violation.

Uncertain, this trial,
implying girl means rape;
authenticity damned
in a jury's evidence.

Her indelible memory shared –
a body, partially clothed,
awash with blood, semen and tears:
attracting less interest

than the translation
of a forties French film,
woman in silk stockings,
chemise and chignon.

Allow me, gentlemen,
to sum up by seeing
the filthy irony, the sanctimony,
the bastard hypocrisy, projected

on your screens of fantasy
subtitled 'she asked for it'.

Daddies' Girls

Maura Johnston

'Who's Daddy's girl? She looks
Just like her Mammy.' Good.
He'll notice me and I'll
Be the beloved child.
'She's got a boyfriend. Yes.
You know his family, at least
His mother. I'm pleased.'
His touch, his smile release
A catch. I'm normal.
I've done the right thing for a
Change. 'What a lovely
House! So big! Above
The usual run. He must
Make a regular fuss
Of you.' O yes, I know.
He's nine-to-five, no
Working late. I've all
Mod. cons. Small
Wonder that my smile
Is pasted permanently.
'Isn't she sweet! Just
Like her Mammy. The first
Gets so much attention
Don't forget to mention
That you love him too.'
Fingers clutch me smoothly.
The circle tightens. Together
We can break out. Daddies' girls.

Him

Carol Scanlon

She called him that,
Or 'your father'.
We wondered at the silence
Greeting us each 5 o'clock,
The moods behind the Telegraph,
The grunts of displeasure,
The cracked plate.

No one could interrupt the misery
Or understand it.
Of course – what excuse could there be for
His dinner being late and the water being cold and
His family for just being there!
(My mother on all fours
Careful not to catch his eye.)

How to stop it –
I know!
If I could tell him I won the three-legged,
Had found a fiver,
Passed the 11 plus…
Would that make him smile,
Make him love us?

Father Figure

Maura Johnston

The lost-soul moan of wind in the wires
And benweed poking patterns in the grass
Like jaundiced fingers of doom
Sift through my shifting memories
That settle in a mottled morass
And twist new shapes in this room.

I almost feel the brittle crust
Of cold that made the hurricane
Clam in my hand, and
Slid his shadow monstrous
On the meal house wall, pinned
There prosperous, the self made man.

We saw an owl once, in the front field,
Sagged in a secret of feathers, waiting.
That was in the twilight when
He fingered grasses to guage a yield,
Or lovingly leaned on a gate
His acres before him.

We worked the hay for him, trying to make
The music he could with a worn
Wooden rake along a green swathe.
Our notes wavered, got weak.
We are scattered. Alone
I can face him now, unafraid.

One For Sorrow...

Laura Shier

My father had a superstitious fear
Of magpies. In the spring they used to come,
So elegant and smart in black and white,
To strut upon the lawn before the house.
They built their shaggy nest in a tall tree.
He sent a nimble man to climb the height
And dangerously dash it down; and yet
Again they came and walked before the windows.

I do not think that ill-luck followed him;
He died, a fine old man, in his own home,
His loving wife and family at his side.
Now I, with no belief in such omens,
Remembering my father, still salute
The magpies.

From
Tea in a China Cup
Christina Reid

The lights darken on this scene.

    At one side of the stage we see Theresa Duffy, a child of eleven, skipping. She sings 'On the hill there stands a lady, who she is I do not know. All she wants is gold and silver, all she wants is a nice young man.' Beth arrives and they skip together and sing the song again. They sit down, breathlessly.

BETH: Theresa?

THERESA: What?

BETH: You know the way your mammy bought my mammy's china cabinet and all the stuff in it?

THERESA: Yes.

BETH: Well, sure you won't tell anybody about it?

THERESA: Why not?

BETH: Because it's private and my granny says nobody's to know.

THERESA: All right... I think it's rotten-looking anyway.

BETH: My mammy loved it. She used to polish it every day.

THERESA: My daddy says it's daft having all those cups and saucers and things just for looking at.

BETH: That's what my daddy said too.

THERESA: Have you got your new uniform for the grammar school yet?

BETH: Not yet, my mammy's still saving up to pay for it.

THERESA: I got mine last week. You want to see it. Everything's dark green, even the knickers.

BETH: Our uniform's navy blue.

THERESA: Are the knickers navy blue too?

BETH: Yes.

THERESA: Do you know what the big lad down the

street says those sort of knickers are called?

BETH: What?

THERESA: Passion killers.

BETH: What does that mean?

THERESA: I don't know. I asked my mammy and she hit me and made me go to confession.

They sit and ponder this for a moment.

BETH: Aren't your teachers all nuns?

THERESA: Some of them are. They'll all be nuns when I go to the convent grammar school.

BETH: Is it true that they always go around in pairs because one of them's a man?

THERESA: Who told you that?

BETH: My great aunt Maisie.

THERESA: Nuns are women. The men are called monks. Your aunt's having you on.

BETH: She read it in a book that was written by a girl who escaped from a convent.

THERESA: My granny has a book about a rich Protestant landowner, and all these young Catholic girls worked in his big house and they all got babies, so they did.

BETH: Were they married?

THERESA: No they weren't.

BETH: Your granny's head's away. You have to be married to get a baby.

THERESA: I have a cousin who's not married and she got a baby.

BETH: How?

THERESA: I don't know. I asked my mammy about that too, and she hit me again.

The lights darken on the two puzzled children.

Beth as an adult addresses the audience.

BETH: We knew nothing. We found it impossible to get an accurate answer to anything relating to bodily functions. Babies were a gift from God to married women. I asked my great aunt Maisie why God gave more gifts to the Catholics if the Protestants of Ulster were his chosen people. She said it was

36

because the Catholics were greedy. They were
always looking for something for nothing. My
mother did attempt to have a serious talk with me
once, but it was very confusing and embarrassing
for both of us.

*At the other end of the stage Beth, aged eleven, is sitting
on a chair reading a comic. Sarah is ironing. Her
back is to Beth.*

SARAH: Beth?

BETH: What?

SARAH: Don't say what, say pardon.

BETH: Pardon.

SARAH: That's better... I want to explain something to
you... you'll be growing up and there's things you
have to be told... are you listening?

Embarrassed, she keeps her back firmly to Beth.

BETH: Yes mammy.

SARAH: Some time... in the next year or two... there's a
thing that happens to girls of your age... it happens
once a month... you know where you go to the
toilet... down there...

BETH: Yes.

SARAH: Well, once a month... when you start to grow
up... to become a young woman... you get... you
get... a drop of blood comes out of there...

BETH *(startled)***:** Blood?

SARAH: Now there's nothing to worry about. It happens to all women... it's just a part of growing up...
it doesn't do you any harm... it comes for a few
days and then it goes away... until the next month.
When it happens, you tell me, you don't go telling
your father or our Sammy, do you hear?

BETH: Do my daddy and Sammy not know about it?

SARAH: You don't talk to men about that sort of thing,
it's not nice.

BETH: Who will I tell if it happens at school?

SARAH: You'll tell nobody. It's not the sort of thing you
talk about. It's private. It won't be much the first
time it happens. You'll be alright till you get home.

BETH: Will it happen soon?

SARAH: It depends... some girls are earlier than others... with any luck you'll be late startin'... the later the better...

BETH: Why does it happen... what's it for?

SARAH: It's just one of those things women have to put up with... there's a lot of things in this life that women have to put up with, you'll find that out as you get older... and another thing, Beth, when you do get older and maybe go out with boys... don't ever let them do anything that's not nice... always remember, your private parts are your own... do you understand that now?

BETH *(uncertainly):* Yes mammy.

SARAH: That's a good girl.

Relieved that the talk is over, Sarah folds up the ironing board and carries it off without looking at Beth. Beth sits with a puzzled look on her face. She looks down at herself, shrugs, and continues reading her comic.

Lights darken on Beth.

At the other side of the stage the eleven year old Theresa appears in green convent uniform. She is carrying a schoolbag.

She waves and calls towards the darkened part of the stage.

THERESA: Beth! Beth!

Beth steps into the light. she is not in a uniform, just a dress and cardigan. She is also carrying a schoolbag.

THERESA: Mine started, last night, just when I was getting ready for bed.

BETH: Now we're both grown up.

THERESA: Yes.

BETH: Did your mammy cry?

THERESA: No, but she told me I wasn't to wash my hair while I had it or put my feet in cold water, or the blood would all rush to my head and I'd die. Did your mammy cry?

BETH: A wee bit. She said, 'God help you, child, this is the start of all your troubles.'

THERESA: My mammy calls it the curse.

38

BETH: I wish somebody would tell us what it's all about. I mean if it's going to bring us some sort of trouble, do you not think we should know?

THERESA: Sure they never tell you anything.

BETH: I like your uniform. It's lovely.

THERESA: Why are you not going to the grammar school, Beth?

BETH: My mammy can't afford the uniform, but don't be telling anybody, because I'm not allowed to say.

THERESA: All right.

They walk off together.

A Curse

Brenda Murphy

She awoke in stages, aware of the humming sound that filled the space she was in. The fan, they had said. But that was not what had tugged her out of sleep. Cramping pains gripped her lower belly, holding her, then tightening their grip by spasms. A deep ache in the small of her back. She lay huddled, knees drawn up, face to the wall, eyes closed to block out the constantly burning light.

She sat up and looked about her. The yellow dimpled walls covered in graffiti stared back. She coughed and felt the ooze between her legs, the familiar ooze, the heat, the wetness. Her mother called it 'the curse'. A curse it was for her right then.

How long had she been asleep? What time was it? She could smell her own sweat, sniffed under her arm as if to confirm it. She felt a desperate need to wash herself, to be clean again. She took off her shoe, went over to the cell door and banged hard. After a while she heard footsteps, the jangle of keys. The door unlocked, a policeman stood before her.

'What do you want?'

'Can I speak to a policewoman?'

'No.' After a pause, 'There's none here at the minute. Now what is it?' He eyed her impatiently.

'I've taken my period,' she said simply. 'I need some sanitary towels and a wash. I've not been allowed to wash since I was arrested, days ago.'

He looked at her with disgust. 'Have you no shame? I've been married twenty years and my wife wouldn't mention things like that.'

What is the colour of shame? All she could see was red as it trickled down her leg.

'Look, mister, I asked for a policewoman. I'm filthy, I'm bleeding, I need a wash and a change of clothes. Ask them to ring my mother. She'll bring them down for

40

me. I don't think even your wife would stand here and bleed in silence.'

'Don't you foul-mouth my wife, you wee hussy!' His face contorted with rage as he slammed the cell door.

She sat down again on the raised wooden boards and watched the blocked-out window in the ceiling. An hour, maybe two passed. She couldn't tell. Then footsteps again and the cell door opened. The policeman and a policewoman stared in at her.

'Right you, up!' said the woman officer, handing the prisoner a sanitary towel. Her voice was high-pitched and squeaky. 'Follow me and hurry up about it. You have to go to the interview room again.'

They walked along a corridor and a door was opened to reveal a toilet, wash basin and urinal. The stench was overwhelming. The girl went in. The toilet was blocked. She tried to flush it but it didn't work. She put on the sanitary towel then went to the basin. No soap, no towel, no hot water. She splashed her face with water, drying it on the bottom of her sweater.

'Hurry up,' piped the policewoman from the doorway, reluctant to go in any further.

'Look, could you see if I can have a change of clothes and a proper wash? You know what it's like when you have your period.'

The woman officer appeared not to hear, looking away as she repeated, 'Hurry up. You're wanted for interview.'

She stepped past the policewoman, who walked her upstairs to the interview room. It was exactly as she remembered it. Bright, electric, windowless.

From
The Countrywoman
Una Woods

The oil lamp flickered shadows across the white page of
the notebook. She was creating out of words an atmosphere and out of the atmosphere more words. It
seemed as if she was recreating a world, affirming its
existence on the page.

The hydrangea came out in July. Mauve and pink
bunched round in the front garden. I pulled the front
door after me and started down the path. I heard a
chucking sound and saw my mother bent, pulling weeds.
I seemed to be always walking past but that was something in itself.

Nasal snores and guttural sighs competed with each
other in the corner of the caraven. She had counted
three heads when she came in. It was part of the understanding. Any of the children might fall into the bed. She
was the lodger.

There was a wind rasping in the trees above the site,
opening the night. Somewhere a can rattled crookedly.

One night the silence had been broken into, crashed
upon by a hacking and crunching. At the very homes of
the sleeping inhabitants. The unexpected climax of a
feud. Dark men descended from the heights with blunt
and sharp weapons. In the blurred confusion window
glass showered in on bewildered children. Men were
dragged outside and beaten, humiliated in front of their
women, left slabbering out of misshapen jaws into the
muck.

At dawn the women and children stopped wailing
and cleared up. They pulled together and held together.
She worked with them and made countless cups of tea
and when the red flame of the morning sun glowed over
the wounded camp there entered pride and a fierce sense

of drama into the talk. It was war atmosphere.

During lessons in the hut that morning the children drew pictures of men fighting and caravans broken. Intensely filling the pages with sharp colours and the vicious mouths of the attackers. The thought of leaving through fear had diminished in her by mid-morning.

It had been a windy night like tonight. She looked round to where the kettle rattled on the gas ring. She had two cups waiting. She put her notebook away and waited for Jim's tap on the window.

It was strange, the link, the passion that passed between them, only touching and withdrawing. Sometimes it seemed as though it were invented by the other travellers, who smiled and occasionally wiped the tears from their cheeks. Like a song they were singing, nostalgic, out of a country or a white wedding. It was all the same, the distance of one's own past.

The flame made a tiny noise between them and there was the sound of Jim rubbing his cup against his fingers. It was a moment for explanation but there were not the words. Laura was aware of the silent gulf and that it was encouraging her retreat. Yet it annoyed her, the enforced silence, the implication of failure.

'It was only a dance,' she said, to open it up, or lessen the gap. Her words were like sand trickling over the edge. Having no impact.

He took a cigarette from a packet and, striking a match, accentuated the fierce distance of himself. Behind the wavering light his separateness was fixed.

She got up and began to tidy things away, tucking the children in, pushing locks of hair back from damp skin, moving about and doing. He fiddled with her tape recorder, turning it on and off, listening to snatches of songs she had taped on the sight.

'What are you goin' to do with these, Laura?' he asked her.

'I don't know. I might sing them,' she answered.

He gave a self-conscious laugh and then with a childish expression on his face he lifted out the tape and began to examine it as though to discover the secret of the trapped voices. 'Ah, God, the magic country-woman,' he muttered.

She had a blanket wrapped round her when she stood at the door watching him cross over the site. When the lighted end of his discarded cigarette deadened into the blackness she went in and closed the door.

Dear Mother, she wrote, I am coming home. Explanations are vague, they always are, and in a way my decision to come back is like my decision to leave in the first place. Like any decision. But I'm looking forward to it.

Leaving is desertion, she wrote in her notebook. I will not escape the pain of it.

Jim is noticing you growing up, she told Eileen. Eileen blushed. She divided the books from the hut amongst the bewildered children and told the adults she would sing their songs.

When she was walking up the hill she heard the wailing from the site. She stopped and looked down to where the caravans were strewn beneath the trees on her left. When she turned to glance back down the road she saw children carrying each other, coming barefoot up the hill after her.

An Invitation to Dinner

Francine Cunningham

Mother bites
on a bit
of bread
leaving
a hieroglyph
in butter.

Her children
have graduated
to the piano top
and send
fluent
letters.

Now
I can write
only
for those
who speak
my tongue;

like the cordon bleu chef
who prepares meals
for those who
are not
hungry.

Mandrake

Francine Cunningham

Your wit was my cutting.

You planted me
inside that hot house,
stalking in contingency,
not caring to sow
alone.

Rootless
I withered, blanched
before reflex scrutiny,
after-shock of culture.

Quickly acclimatized
you abandoned me,
unwilling to recede
to former temperate.

Soiled,
I've twisted, but grown
hybrid.
In bitter composition

I sank
umbilical
among the widest
imbibing their experience.

Even now fear of being uprooted.

From Myself

Dorothy Gharbaoui

Set in the 1920s and 30s. The Mercers are a wealthy linen family. Mrs Mercer does good works, deeming this to be the duty of a lady in her fortunate position. When Marion, one of her daughters, accepts a scholarship to Oxford against her parents' will, she regards it as a selfish and 'unnatural' action for a girl.

In this scene, many years later, Marion has come home for a visit from London where she has become the successful author of a trilogy on the Renaissance Borgia family. She helps her favourite sister, Rose, to take their elderly maid, Lizzie, to see the Twelfth of July procession. Rose has considerable artistic talent which has never been encouraged by her family.

(Sounds of Twelfth of July procession in Belfast. Band playing 'The Sash' uproariously.)

Lizzie *(ageing but managing to sing softly):* 'It was old, but it was beautiful'.

Rose: Oh, do shut up, Lizzie!

Lizzie: If you don't like it, Miss Rose, what do ye come for?

Rose: Because you're not fit to come out in these crowds on your own. Marian, take her arm and we'll drag her home.

Marian *(amused):* Oh, let her enjoy herself.

Rose: I can't stand this noise.

Marian: It's absolutely perfect pagan ritual.

Rose: It's ghastly.

Marian: Oh, come on for a walk down that avenue, then, and you can pinch somebody's hydrangeas. Lizzie'll be all right. We'll come back for her.

Lizzie: God save us, look at thon wee man dancin' with the banner! Isn't he powerful?

Marian: Now, stay there, Lizzie, and don't get lost! We'll be back soon.

(The noise begins to fade progressively as they walk further away, though it remains faintly in the background. Footsteps at leisure on suburban pavement.)

Rose: Don't you get bored with all this, after London?

Marian: It's a change. *(Laughs)* Anyhow, it's all part of the human condition. What writers like me are supposed to know about.

Rose: But you write about the past.

Marian: People are basically the same now as they were four or five hundred years ago.

Rose: People... I can't be bothered with most of them.

Marian: Would you rather have been a bumblebee, Rose, or a butterfly, or a lizard basking in the sun? Like the ones I see in Italy.

Rose: No. None of them lives long enough.

Marian: What would you rather be, then?

Rose: Dunno. Myself. If people would only let me alone.

Marian: But what is you, Rose? What goes on inside that cardigan-clad bosom of yours?

(Footsteps stop.)

Rose: Stop being stupid!

Marian: I want to know. I really do. Always have.

Rose: Leave go.

Marian: Why is it more important to you to stare at that tree? I bet you're wishing you had your sketchpad with you.

Rose: I never saw one with a branch hanging just like that.

Marian: And that's important?

Rose: It is, to me.

Marian: What about me? Am I not important to you?

Rose: You do go on about things. Why don't you leave it alone?

Marian: Leave what alone?

Rose: Analysing everything.

Marian: We're sisters.

Rose: Come on! Lizzie'll get lost.

(Footsteps start again.)

Marian: Does it ever occur to you I might get lost?

Rose: Oh, shut up!

Marian: You always said that ever since we were little. When anyone embarrassed you or tried to get near you. And you're still saying it when you're over thirty, and I'll be over it soon too. What's being a sister about, Rose? Why does it stop people loving each other? ...Didn't it ever occur to you that families should love each other?

Rose *(embarrassed):* Well, they do... I suppose.

Marian: But you won't even let me touch you. You've just pushed me away.

Rose: Those people are staring.

Marian: I don't care.

Rose: This is Belfast. Not London. You can do what you like there.

Marian: What do you imagine I do there?

Rose: Go to grand parties... get invited to lecture to people... write this book. You're getting to be famous, aren't you? That's what you wanted.

Marian: Was it?

Rose: What else do you want?

Marian: Most of the time, you know, I'm anchored at a desk in a study, up the stairs in a flat in Maida Vale.

Rose: Well?

Marian: Using this so-called marvellous brain of mine.

Rose: You wanted to.

Marian: At the beginning it was exciting. Sometimes it still is. But, Rose, it was scary too, like... do you remember? ...putting your feet in an icy sea for the first time. And knowing you either venture out, or turn back and stay on the shore. Rose, I had to try it, I had to go to Oxford, then I got to Florence. I couldn't turn back.

Rose: No one stopped you.

Marian: But shouldn't they have? Shouldn't someone have said maybe I was meant to look after a man, and bring up children?

Rose: Mama said so.

Marian: No one really told me what it was all about. The way they said it, it sounded like prison... Even when he talked about it...

49

Rose: He asked you, didn't he?

Marian: But he didn't wait. Why, Rose? Why did he have to marry Evelyn, of all people?

(Footsteps slow a little.)

Rose: He needed a wife and you weren't there... Don't see why you should worry. Never wanted a man myself. Look at Evelyn covering herself with cream every night so she won't get wrinkles.

Marian: Are they happy?

Rose: How do I know? Pity about the miscarriages. *(Footsteps stop.)* Gosh, I can never pass this garden. It's miraculous.

Marian: Sometimes I think... or wish... am I deceiving myself? ...it was the nearest he could get to marrying me. *(Footsteps take off again, rather fast.)* Wait for me, Rose!

Rose *(walking briskly):* You're not so clever. You're stupid.

Marian *(breathless):* I know.

Rose *(not listening):* People are stupid. They think they're unique and they can do everything their own way, different from everyone else. Birds and flowers have more sense. They've got a pattern to their lives and they just follow it.

Marian: But why couldn't we have loved each other? All of us. Why were we all so afraid of expressing anything except a sense of duty, and virtue, and...? Wait Rose. *(Footsteps stop)* Please! Do you understand why I started to write about Cesare and Lucrezia and...?

Rose *(bluntly cutting in):* Mama has never got over it. That's why she won't go out with you anywhere when you come home.

Marian: But they loved each other. All of them. All right, it was incest.

Rose: Sh!

Marian: I'll scream it if I want to. It was unnatural, all right, brothers and sisters and fathers and daughters making love. But it was something. Not like us. Ingrown on our own feelings. How can we love

50

other people, Rose, if we don't love ourselves? And... don't you see? ...our family is... ourselves. Why did Mama make us like that?

Rose: You and Mama... why can't you be at peace?

Marian: She did it to you too, Rose, can't you see? We were the same, really, only you got kept at home. We should have been together, you and I. *(Footsteps start again.)* No, don't run away. Don't be frightened because I'm saying what I feel, aloud. Rose... I really only come home to see you.

Familiars

Ann W. Gleave

Barren as the lakeland fell
from which I germed,
cold as the cotton mill windows
by which I ran
and sooty dark as the cobbles
over which
the northern rains
glistened,
I lie,
listening to night whispers.
Tangled and knotted
as a pointed shawl
the stitches of days
fade into muted colour
each one meaning
a story now lost
beneath Pendle Hill –
consigned to the
dank canal –
beaten into sparks
by the clogs' steel,
huddled in doorways
back to back.

Barren,
I lie,
in a fair country
and pick dry autumn leaves
from the street floor.

Familiars
ever with me
enter rooms
sleep on stairs,
dry out the garden grasses
by day.

Still the barren heath hold
does not give way
and I lie,
catching rain
in a frosty morning
till the glass overflows,
pictures fade,
walls dampen and sag
and heather is all
the colour
of weather
in Bowland.

October 1978

From Lay Up Your Ends
A monologue by Marie Jones

Belle, one of the leaders in the 1911 Belfast strike, gives voice to her growing awareness and understanding of the mill workers' plight.

'I'm going round now to Big Jim McClenaghan's wake. Do you know he used to be the best luckin' hackler that ever walked York Street, till the pouce got him. Thirty-five years of age, he's happy done for. The Lord did him a favour, cos I've watched many another suffer on. Coughin' their guts up, not being able to get a breath with the oul flax, it's a terrible death. But I'll tell you this, there's no chance of Bingham (the mill owner) being laid up with the mill fever. Thirty years I have wrought in that mill and I've hardly ever clapped eyes on him. He lives in a big house up the Antrim Road. I seen it for meself, going home on the tramcar from Glengormley. Jesus, me eyes near dropped out of my head. Him, sitting up there on his arse with all that money, probably big lumps of steak on his plate every night for his dinner, and Big Jim McClenaghan lying in a box through doing his day's work. Oh God that's not fair. But if I was to say that to Bingham he would just laugh at me. But he'd laugh on the other side of his face if every man, woman and child that works in this mill said we're not going through them gates, not until we've got what's due to us. Then he would listen to us, he would have to, for when you think about it, he's got a hell of a lot to lose. Look at us, look round ye, what do ye see? Prosperous Belfast, eh? What have we got to lose? You know, I'm not too good at the sums, but I'll tell you what I do know – you can't take nothin' away from nothin'.'

54

Leaving

Anne-Marie Reilly

Ever since I can remember my mother wanted to move house. 'Up the road' was what she called it. I wasn't sure where 'up the road' was, but even then I knew it would be somewhere wonderful. I think it must have been my mother who sowed the seeds of wanderlust and discontent in me, although what she longed for was a far cry from what I eventually yearned after.

We lived in a small rented house in a street off the Falls Road. Gradually I learned that 'down the Falls' was anywhere below the Falls Park and 'up the road', the longed-for paradise, was anywhere further than the Falls Park. My aunt lived there, my mother's younger sister. She had 'married well'. Her husband drove a car. My father disliked them intensely. They had achieved material success, my father never would. I loved going there, so did my mother. They had a garden and a bathroom and a proper sitting-room with a piano in it. My uncle Peter played the piano and the banjo and was great fun. He was never crabby like my father, although my aunt was an absolute 'targe'. She didn't allow him to smoke his pipe indoors and always spoke sharply to him as though he were another child. As the years passed his own children treated him the same way and I used to wish he were my father so that I could be good to him. He and my mother adored each other, the other two were well met. They fought and argued and my aunt was the only one I knew who could get the better of my father. I often wished they could all swap over so that my mother was married to uncle Peter.

Our street was small and parochial and very clannish. Everyone gossiped and borrowed and visited. My mother stayed apart from all this, she wouldn't be there for long, she hoped. When I was born she'd been there fifteen years already and still she wanted desperately to live somewhere else. My father, as usual, was the problem. He was frightened of the responsibility of buying a house. He might have to sacrifice his social life and he wasn't prepared to do that. That my mother was unhappy did not affect him in any way. He had all he wanted, he could not understand her need. She wanted to bring us up in a better area, she wanted to be part of a more socially acceptable environment. All that was beyond my father. As the years passed my mother grew more and more embittered. The chances of owning her own home faded with advancing age, but still she could not accept, nor ever become part of the community we lived in. In some ways my sisters and I had stayed aloof also, always waiting for the day when we would move 'up the road'. My sisters married and bought houses with bathrooms and gardens. In some ways this compensated my mother but in others it made her resent my father even more. They had achieved in no time what she could not in a lifetime.

Life is nothing if not ironic. My mother finally got to move, and to exactly where, thirty years before, she would have chosen to go. Our street was one of the first to be burned and my parents had to run from the house they had lived in for thirty-two years, clutching a very few personal belongings.

They were re-housed in a top floor maisonette 'up the road'. What my mother had hoped to escape from came with her. 'Up the road' became the new Catholic ghetto following the gutting of many streets in the Lower Falls. In the panic of leaving my mother lost a navy suit, bought for a wedding. She talked for weeks about that suit, never mentioning once the home she had lost. I can still feel the shock of finding my father in tears as he heard over the radio which homes had been destroyed.

They have never settled in their new home. They won't buy a fitted carpet 'in case they move', or new furniture 'in case they move'. Yet I know my mother has long since given up hope of that much-wanted house. Strangely, it's for my father's sake that she keeps up the pretence. The consequence of my mother's life is now surfacing in mine. I won't waste time longing for something better, I'll go out and fight for it and that is bringing its own heartache.

The Bonfire

Geraldine Reid

Flames cascade
Crushing the night
Against a reddened
Bloody sky
Where memories
Paddle past
In a clouded canoe.
Silhouetted hearts
Stand in the heat
Of hate.
Bare and raw
Burning away...

Heading Home

Mary McGowan

A glazed, rain-running window-pane screening the English countryside slipping by. Not that I can see much in the darkness of this night, not that I care anyway. The train rattles through small towns whose ears never hear it, whose eyes never blink open. They don't sit up in bed and shake their fists. In time, I too would grow accustomed to this never-ending stream of metal passing my home. But I don't want to. This is not my home.

Onwards through the night to the hesitant dawn of Scotland. All around me contorted bodies begin to squirm and groan as the pale light brings them back to life, as if in some grotesque parody of Judgement Day. I too am stiff, but I don't mind so much. The back of the journey is broken. London is a night, a lifetime away. I light my first cigarette of the morning and immediately regret it. I don't stub it out, though.

Barren, brown-green hills, sheep-dotted farms and still, black lakes become clear as a new day asserts itself. As we approach Stranraer everyone begins to gather their bits and pieces of luggage together. Do I look as dishevelled and tired as they do? When the train shudders to a halt, the unspoken bond between us is snapped as people clamber from the carriage and hurry towards the dormant boat.

The wind waters my eyes and reddens my cheeks as I stand in line, waiting my turn to bounce along the plastic-covered passageway to the boat's car deck. The police are questioning two boys as the rest of us file by, too tired to feel sorry for anyone but ourselves.

As I stand on deck, behind me Stranraer is beginning to shake itself from sleep and smoke rises from a few chimneys. I imagine people sitting to their breakfasts, making ready for work, sending their children to school. They know nothing of me, a stranger passing through as so many must do each day. I walk to the front of the boat. Ahead of me is the open sea and as I stare across it, I forget the shouts of the crew, the scavenging seagulls, the creaks and rattles of unseen chains, the hum of the engines. I think of the violence, the fear, the warmth, the laughter and love, my family, my friends and my enemies, all those strands which time has woven together to form my home, Derry. As the boat rumbles to life, my heart is glad to be heading home.

Five Notes After a Visit
Anne Devlin

I begin to write.

The first note:

'You were born in Belfast?' the security man at the airport said.

'Yes.'

'What is the purpose of your visit there?'

To be with my lover. Well, I didn't say that. I had written 'research' on the card he was holding in his hand. I remind him of this.

'I would like *you* to answer the questions,' he says.

'I am doing research.'

'Who is your employer?'

'Self.' I stick to my answers on the card.

'Oh! The idle rich,' he says.

'I live on a grant.'

I might have expected this. It happens every time I cross the water. But I will never get used to it.

'Who is paying for your ticket?'

'I am.'

'What a pity.' He smiles. 'And what have you been doing in England all this time?'

'Living.' Trying.

'There was a bomb in Oxford Street yesterday. Some of your countrymen.'

Two feet away some passengers with English accents are saying goodbye to their relatives. A small boy holding his mother's hand is smiling. Two feet between the British and the Irish in the airport lounge; I return the child's smile. Two feet and seven hundred years.

'He's a small man doing a small job!' Stewart says, when he meets me at the other side. 'Forget about him.' I won't. 'Now don't be cross with me. But you could save yourself a lot of trouble if you'd only write British under nationality.'

'I think –' I start to say, but don't finish. Next time I'll write 'don't know'.

I come back like a visitor. I always do. And I'm treated like one. On the Black Mountain road from the airport it is getting dark, when the taxi driver says, 'Do you see that orange glow down there? Just beyond the motorway?'

'Yes.'

'Those are the lights of the Kesh.'

Like a football stadium to the uninitiated.

'And just up there ahead of us,' he points to a crown of white lights on Divis ridge, 'that's the police observatory station. That's where they keep the computer.'

'Is it?'

'I had to do a run up there once. But I never got past the gates.'

We plunge down Hannastown Hill in the dark towards the lights of a large housing estate. If I don't speak in this taxi, perhaps he'lll think I'm English.

'What road is this?' Stewart asks, as we pass my parents' house. His father is a shipyard worker.

SINN FEIN IS THE POLITICAL WING OF THE PROVISIONAL IRA is painted on the gable. WESTMINSTER IS THE POLITICAL WING OF THE BRITISH ARMY.

'This is Andersonstown,' the taxi driver says.

There is barbed wire on the flowerbeds in my father's garden. A foot patrol trampled his crocuses last spring. Tomorrow I'll go and tell them I've come home. But not yet. Stewart isn't keen.

'They won't approve of me,' he says. 'I've been married once before. They'll persuade you to go back to England.'

'They won't!' I insist. But I have the same old fear. His first wife lives in East Belfast.

Tuesday 10th January 1984

The second note:

I am looking at the bus that will take me to my mother. Through the gates I can see the others waiting

61

too. I hear myself say: 'Mother, I've come back!'; and I hear her ask me, 'Why?'

I have let him lure me from my undug basement garden in an English town; one egg in the fridge and the dregs of milk; my solitude wrapped around me like a blanket for those six years until he came – and presented me with the only kind of miracle I ever really believed in.

I hear her ask me, 'Why?'

I remember the summer months, our breakfasts at lunchtime in my garden, our evening meals on the raft, my bed. When term began again, he said: 'I've got a job in Belfast. Will you come and live with me?'

'Oh, I can't go back,' I said. 'I can't – live without you,' I tell him at the airport when I arrive.

I hear her ask me why?

My house is empty and the blinds are down. The letters slip into the hall unseen. The tanks will still turn onto the Whiteladies Road out of the Territorial Army Barracks and pass the BBC. And the black cab driver will drive someone else from the station. 'Where to?' Blackboy Hill.

A For Sale notice stands in the uncut grass..

I hear her ask me why? I turn away from the stop.

Wednesday 1st February 1984
I have not kept an account of the days in between because I am too tired after work to write. And anyway I go to bed with him at night.

The third note:

It is the third day of the third week of my visit. I am working in the library.

'On the 1st of January 1957 the Bishop of Down and Connor's Relief Fund for Hungarian Refugees amounted to £19,375 0s 6d. Further contributions in a daily newspaper for that morning include: Sleamish Dancing Club, £5; Bon Secours Convent, Falls Road, £10; The John Bosco Society for the Prevention of Communism, £25; A sinner, Anonymous –'

'Love?'

'£5. Three months later, in April of the same year,

62

the Lord Mayor of Belfast welcomed the first 500 refugees. It was the only issue on which the people of
Belfast East and West agreed.'

'Love.'

He is standing at my table.

'Oh, I'm sorry, I didn't see you.'

'Love. My wife's just rung. I'll have to go and see
her. She was crying on the phone. She wants to discuss us
getting back together. If only you knew how angry this
makes me!'

'Will you tell her about me?'

Below the library window voices reach me from the
street. The students are assembling for a march. They
shoulder a black coffin: RIP EDUCATION is chalked
in on the side.

Maggie. Maggie. Maggie. Out! Out! Out!

Police in bulletproof jackets flank the thin demonstration through the square. The wind tosses the voice
back and forth; I only catch an odd phrase here and
there: 'Our comrades in England... The trade union
movement in this country...'

'We have to keep a low profile for a while,' he said.
'And don't answer the phone in case it's her.'

When I was young I think, watching the demonstration pass. I must have been without fear. I make a
resolution: I will go there after dark.

Thursday 2nd February 1984

The Feast of the Purification. And James Joyce's birth-
day. I always remember it.

This is the fourth note:

He is scraping barnacles off the mussels when I
come back after midnight. 'Where were you?' he asks.

'I went to see my mother.'

'How was it?'

'She asked the usual questions. Did I still go to
Mass? She said she'd pray for me.'

'Did you tell her about me?'

'I talked about my research: The Flight of Hungarian Refugees to Belfast in '57. Can't think why. She said when I was leaving: "Keep your business to yourself". She was talking about you.'

'My wife cried when I told her. She thinks it's a phase I'm going through – and I'll get over it.'

There are pink and red carnations in a jug on the table, the man-next-door's music is coming through the walls. A trumpet. Beethoven. I'm getting good at that.

'He's obsessive,' Stewart says. 'He's played that piece since ten o'clock.'

At the table, I make a mistake: I push my soup away, I'm not as hungry as I thought.

'Go back! Go back to England then! You said you *could* live with me.'

'I am trying.'

When I wake the smell of garlic reaches me from the bottom of the stairs. It was the mussel soup he lifted off the table. 'Go back! Go back to England! You're not anybody's prisoner!'

'I am trying!'

Mussel shells, garlic, onion, tomato paste, tomatoes and some wine, he threw into the kitchen. But the garlic hangs over everything this morning; and the phone is ringing in a room downstairs.

In some places, he said last night, amid the broken crockery, before a marriage they smash the dishes, they break the plates to frighten off the ghosts. Perhaps this is necessary after all.

When he wakes, I whisper: 'Love, I'll stay.'

'I've found you again,' he says.

The phone is still ringing in a room downstairs. It is 2.30 in the afternoon.

'Send your Fenian girlfriend back where she belongs, or we'll give her the works and then you.'

He is staring at the clock.

'I wonder how they knew?' he says.

'The estate agent has been writing to me from England. It was too much trouble to explain the difficulty of it. The postman would notice a Catholic name in this street. The sorters in the Post Office too. Or maybe it was the man collecting for the football pools –'

'Football pools?'

'The other night a man came to the door, he asked me to pick four teams or eight, I can't remember now. Then he asked me to sign it.'

'You should have given my name.'

'I did. But I don't know anything about football. And I think I gave myself away when –'

'What?'

'I picked Liverpool. Or it could have happened at the launderette when I left the washing in. They asked: 'What name?' And I forgot. Or it could have been the taxi I got last night from here to –'

'I suppose they would have found out some time.' He is sitting on the bed.

'Could it have been – your wife?'

He looks hurt: 'I never told her that!' he says. 'I suppose they would have found out some time. I think I'd better call the police.'

I get up quickly: 'Do you mind if I get dressed and bath and make the bed before you do?'

'Why?'

'Because they'll come round and look at every-thing.'

I am packing a large suitcase in the attic where we sleep when he comes upstairs.

'The police say that anyone who really meant a threat wouldn't ring you up beforehand. They're not coming round.'

'Listen. I want you to take me to the airport. And I want you to pack a bag as well.'

'I'm teaching tomorrow,' he says. 'Please leave something behind, love. That black dress of yours. The one I like you in.'

It is still hanging in the wardrobe. I leave my scent in the bathroom and on his pillow.

'It's just so that I know you'll come back.'

At 3.40 we are ready to leave the house. The street

is empty when we open the door. The curtains are drawn.

'We're a bit late,' he tells the driver. 'Can you get us to the airport in half an hour?'

In the car he kisses me and says: 'No one has ever held my hand so tightly before.'

'What will you do?' I ask, as I'm getting on the plane.

'I'll have to give three months notice.'

'Do it.'

'Teaching jobs are hard to come by,' he says, looking around. 'Whatever this place is – it's my home.'

5.45. Heathrow. Without him I walk from the plane. Who are they watching now? Him or me? Suddenly a man steps out in front of me. Oh Jesus!

'Have you any means of identification? What is the purpose of your visit...?'

Friday 3rd February 1984

The fifth note.

A bell is ringing. I go cautiously to the door. I have slept with all the lights on. I see a man through the glass. He is wearing a combat jacket. This is England, I remind myself. The milkman is smiling at me.

'I saw your lights,' he says.

I tell him I've come back and will he please leave one pint every other day.

He tells me his son's in Northern Ireland in the Army. 'No jobs,' he shouts, walking down the path. 'Were you on holiday?'

'No, I was working.'

The bottles clink in the crate.

'It's well for some.'

He is angry, I begin to think, because I do not drive a milkfloat.

I am shopping again for one. At closing time I go out to the supermarket. It is just getting dark. There are two hundred people gathered in the road outside the shopping precinct. A busker is playing a love song. The police are turning away at the entrance the ones who haven't noticed.

'What is it?' I ask a woman who is waiting at a stop.

'A bomb scare. It's the third one this week.'

I should think before I speak.

'There were 14 people killed in London, in a bomb in a store.'

I am hoping that she hasn't noticed. Some of your countrymen?

Then she says, 'Doesn't matter what nationality you are, dear. We all suffer the same.'

The busker is playing a love song. I am shopping again for one.

Noday. Nodate 1984
I keep myself awake all night so I am ready when they come.

Phantoms

Ann W. Gleave

Imaginary
even the betrayal
imaginary.
No solid foot
has passed the door
no letter loose
in transit – there's
no welcome hearth
empty, waiting.
Even the fears
come explained away;
no real spider in the bath.
No madman
in the unlit stair-well;
just shadows
in the moon's light.
No studied rejections;
just short words
in an envelope
changeling;
just box files
of regrets
and commiseration.

Imaginary
even the past that glows
in memory
to feed on.

Imaginary
the tears
to flood the present.

All is a reflection
oily and smooth
as a straining smile

fixed
in shock.

All is breathless
as the air grows thin,
the sun pales
and the mornings arrive
misty and cold.

Imaginary friends
dazzle socially
and draw into the ring
intellect crowned with kindness –
imaginary
the gleanings
they leave behind.
Phantoms,
they sweep away all trace
of footsteps,
cling to each word,
pick clean
the imaginary bones.

Selvedge

Francine Cunningham

I glanced
at our hands
woven, locked, as
if in shared prayer,
and presently failed
to remember
whose fingers were whose.

A Closed Book

Medbh McGuckian

Some stones hold light, others reflect it;
That is why you are like the sort of door
There is always somebody at; that is
Your real reason for sparing me, as if
You were kissing poetry itself, a name
And promises on the fly-leaf of a
Favourite book. I do not close, I have
Closed already, like the year's
Delayed adolescence creating its own
Winter, a tumour in the throat
That you have to treat like sleeplessness.

Someday, in my house proper, sweeping
Up leaves from far fewer hedges, the ghost
Orchids half-sitting, unspoilt by the intelligence
Of church-bells, I may say how needless
That double set of curtains, the third
Knot on my cord, beside the passion of
The moment that remains the passion
Of the moment, medieval, modern,
The held-in consequence of some dethroning sleep.

The Old Excuse

Bernadette Ross

I love the way you share the sheets
with me, covering every inch.
But you are like a landlord
showing me around your house,
smiling, opening and closing doors for me –
suddenly suggesting payment in advance.
Would you be surprised if I told you
that all I want to do is sleep?

From **A Furnished Room**
Janet McNeill

(When Kate Bennett married, she knew how deeply her husband had loved his first wife, Helen. At the top of the house was Helen's room, still as much hers as it was on the day she died. Then Kate let the room furnished, and the Bennetts' life together changed its course.)

At last he turned for home. Some of the shops at the cross-roads were still lighted. A group of girls, arm-in-arm, exclaimed and pointed in front of a draper's window. From a snack bar came a trickle of music and the smell of coffee. It was a familiar, out-dated tune, with a commonplace nostalgia, but he had shared it with Helen. Boys outside a sweet-shop laughed and whistled at a passing skirt. The door of the public-house, red-blinded, swung open and closed again on the smell of spirits and tobacco smoke and the stir of voices.

The florist's window was empty, but for the florist himself, who was kneeling, taking flowers from a green pail, and setting them in display vases. He worked quickly and skilfully. The flowers were roses, long-stemmed red roses.

The man was surprised when Andrew came into the shop and spoke to him. The last customer searched through his pockets, setting the money down on the counter as he found it.

'Twelve shillings – no, here's a note – give me as many roses as this will buy.'

He pushed the money over.

'Lovely, aren't they?' the florist said, counting out the roses, anxious to justify, or at least to regularize this odd transaction, 'lovely roses. A pity to miss them. And so fresh.'

'No, not a box,' his customer said, 'just give them to me in a bunch.'

They made a big bunch.

'A bit clumsy, isn't it?' the man suggested, trying to roll enough tissue paper round them to keep the stems from dripping. 'And you'd better be careful, or the heads will snap. A box would have been better.'

He handed over the awkward bundle reluctantly.

Andrew came home with quickening excitement. He wanted to see Kate's face when he gave her the roses. Kate's face, not Helen's. Kate. Kate. He imagined her thin pale face, as she breathed in the scent of the flowers, her mouth pouted above them.

There was no sound at all as, for the second time that evening, he turned the key in his door and swung it open. The light in the sitting-room was on, but no one was there. He came back into the hall and listened.

'Kate! Kate!' No one answered.

Kate!' He stood in the hall, calling, with his arms full of roses. 'Kate!'

Fear gripped him suddenly, and he came noisily up the stairs, shouting as he came, 'Kate! Kate! Where are you?

He heard her stir in the dim nursery, and heard Jackie turn and wail.

'Kate – are you there?'

'Andrew! You've woken him,' her thin voice reproached him. 'You've woken him. He's been shouting ever since I put him down. I had to lift him. I had to. Then I got him to sleep and you came in, and now –'

She rocked the child. 'There! There!' He knew by her voice that she was crying.

He didn't go in. He stood out there on the landing, all the fire gone out of him, feeling for the first time the thorns of the roses cutting into his fingers. One of them had drawn blood. He pulled out his handkerchief and dabbed at it clumsily.

'There! There!' Kate's voice, still in weary conscientious monotone, went on, inside the nursery door. Jackie's crying sank to a whimper. 'There! There!'

He was turning to go downstairs again, when he was aware of Miss Whittaker coming up. She was slipping lightly up beside the banisters, still buttoned up in her long waterproof, wearing her hat and gloves.

'Oh – excuse me, Mr Bennett.'

He thrust the roses at her. 'Here, Miss Whittaker, these roses – they're for you.'

Her surprise and pleasure were ludicrous.

'For me, Mr Bennett?'

She gaped at him.

'Yes, yes. Go on – take them.' He pushed the flowers towards her with distaste and impatience, glad to be rid of them.

'Oh, but really –'

Her gloved fingers fumbled nervously at the stalks and gripped his hands instead. At last they were disentangled.

'Aren't they beautiful? Really beautiful! I don't know how I can ever thank you, Mr Bennett.'

He was glad when her flurry of gratitude was over and she went up on to the landing, holding the flowers in front of her, like a votive offering. He could not smell their perfume. Now she had turned up the last flight of stairs.

Quickly, so that he would not hear the door of her room open and close again, he went downstairs to find the food that Kate would have prepared for him.

He was eating it beside the last of the fire when Kate was suddenly at the door, childish in her dressing-gown.

'Andrew, I'm sorry! – I'm sorry!'

He took her up to bed, and later lay holding her, until something of his warmth had reached her cold body. He didn't ask her why she was sorry – sorry because she had introduced Miss Whittaker into the house? – sorry because she had scolded him this evening? – sorry because she had married him? He didn't ask. But he knew, without being told, that while her body was glad of the comfort his warmth gave it, her mind found it a fault that she could accept it.

The Moon Mother

Medbh McGuckian

Twice-lost colonial, making inroads
On my sleep, till I go round with the
Machinery, however can I trust
Your jagged growing, the gender you assume
On a given day? Unmothered by
This extra weight, and jealous of
Your wiriness, I polish the same
Place on the table over and over,
Not regretful of the huts where
The bloodless, blanched gardenia
Stains around the edges when it's touched,
But forming messages to wrap
The braided moon in her dwindling,
Deflowered, self-possessed, aware
Exactly when the floor would act that way.

A Month's Mind
Medbh McGuckian

It's not for nothing at a month's mind
The white hare warms the shrubbery behind the house,
The old world crazy to a thread, the new one
Sharp at both corners, and the roses
Blooming, serrated, in the light,
The crippled hay leaning towards winter.

In my most self-negative mood, not
An egg under my roof, I certify
My detriment of pain, make myself scarce
To fellow such a variable star –
The ice that's grown for an hour,
And cracked with learning.

Nervous Breakdown

Janet Shepperson

In the grey jagged street, things got faster, faster,
the kids dodged round corners, swung from the
      scaffolding,
their mother calling them, dropping carrier bags,
hair in her eyes, the fence she held on to swaying,
a cigarette to steady her nerves in the bulging kitchen,
Mark and Darren screaming, TV blaring and lurching,
the creaking gate in the overgrown garden, uselessly
      banging.

Forty-five minutes in the doctor's waiting room,
ten minutes looking at the line between his eyes.
Blood pressure, stress and prescriptions.
The tablets began to blur her world's hard edges,
slower, slower,
no response she made to the bright smiles
till grey moments later.
Sliding, sleepy,
unable any more to keep up with the children's laughter,
the noises in the street went on without her.

Then the day the water wouldn't flow.
Taps banged like machine guns, nothing came out.
The sink full of greasy dishes.
She sat, stared at the fat congealing,
rattled the taps, looked round helplessly.
A fly buzzed in the empty kitchen.
On the floor, looking up at crooked chair legs,
she lay with her head sideways, waiting.

★★★★★★

They held her hands under the tap,
her hands wet and sparkling,
no use, she remained convinced,
she said the house had no water.

78

In the hospital, trees arched at the windows,
fields, flowers, nettles, crows in the listless afternoon,
curtains hushing round the beds, magazines,
everything trim and well-kept, even the visitors.
She was very quiet and good, she agreed with everyone,
smiled distantly at nurses' briskness, her kids'
      uneasiness,
felt safe, like the middle piece of a jigsaw,
the one with half a rose bush, locked up with all the
      others,
she would never go back to the house that had no water.

It was there in her mind, a torrent,
crashing, shimmering, thundering, carrying down trees
      and buildings,
it sang, it swirled and silvered and shouted,
she couldn't put picture or words to it,
she could hear it, see it, in her blood she could feel it,
all the wildness and fear, magic and rejoicing,
more clear and strong than her family's careful voices,
more urgently bringing back the long-drowned feelings,
the faces of childhood swimming up to her, into her.

★★★★★★

But only she could see it.
So much noise inside her, outside her so much silence,
never again would she hear traffic rumbling, children
      playing,
unless her eyes could lose sight of the glimmering water,
her ears forget to hear the waves within her,
her blood lose the rhythm it shared with the singing
      river.

Frizelle Pump

Mary Twomey

Useless now it stands
Not even connected to a well
A scratching post for cattle.
Rusted remnant
Of a long forgotten settlement.
I envy them their water-drawing
Sense of achievement felt
As they cupped
The pocked ball-handle
And watched the spout
Expectantly
One flailing arm
Quickening its rhythm
As the time draws near
And just when all seems up
Mercifully it comes.
A trickle at first
Then fast and effortlessly it flows
Thrashing and uncontrollable
Filling the banded wooden bucket
And more
Dark-staining
The dusty ground around.
In fat puddling globules
Then it is time
To carry the heavy bucket
Water-brimming
Home again.
And think how worthwhile
The labour was
After all.

Moselle

Ann W. Gleave

Hearth waited silently
nodding with fresh flowers.
Olives scented the room
and faceted glass waited for
the wine.

I've swept out the
last dry leaf,
and now
a lingering taste
of kiss
lays the dust
in my mouth.

Music man,
you feed me in droplets
while I long for the river.

The Wall-Reader

Fiona Barr

'Shall only our rivers run free?' The question jumped out
from the cobbled wall in huge white letters, as The
People's taxi swung round the corner at Beechmount.
'Looks like paint is running freely enough down here,'
she thought to herself, as other slogans glided past in
rapid succession. Reading Belfast's grim graffiti had
become an entertaining hobby for her, and she often
wondered, was it in the dead of night that groups of boys
huddled round a paint tin daubing walls and gables with
tired political slogans and clichés. Did anyone ever see
them? Was the guilty brush ever found? The brush is
mightier than the bomb, she declared inwardly, as she
thought of how celebrated among journalists some lines
had become. 'Is there a life before death?' Well, no one
had answered that one yet, at least, not in this city.

The shapes of Belfast crowded in on her as the taxi
rattled over the ramps outside the fortressed police barracks. Delapidated houses, bricked-up terraces. Rosy-
cheeked soldiers, barely out of school, and quivering
with high-pitched fear. She thought of the thick-lipped
youth who came to hijack the car, making his point by
showing his revolver under his anorak, and of the others,
jigging and taunting every July, almost sexual in their
arrogance and hatred. Meanwhile, passengers climbed
in and out at various points along the road, manoeuvring
between legs, bags of shopping and umbrellas. The taxi
swerved blindly into the road. No Highway Code here.
As the woman's stop approached, the taxi swung up to
the pavement, and she stepped out.

She thought of how she read walls – like tea-cups,
she smiled to herself. Pushing her baby in the pram to
the supermarket, she had to pass under a motorway
bridge that was peppered with lines, some in irregular
lettering with the paint dribbling down the concrete,

82

others written with felt-tip pen in minute secretive hand. A whole range of human emotions splayed itself with persistent anarchy on the walls. 'One could do worse than be a reader of walls,' she thought, twisting Frost's words. Instead, though, the pram was rushed past the intriguing mural with much gusto. Respectable house-wives don't read walls!

The 'Troubles', as they were euphemistically named, remained for this couple as a remote, vaguely irritating wart on their life. They were simply ordinary (she often groaned at the oppressive banality of the word), middle-class, and hoping the baby would marry a doctor, thereby raising them in their autumn days to the select legions of the upper class. Each day their lives followed the same routine – no harm in that sordid little detail, she thought. It helps structure one's existence. He went to the office, she fed the baby, washed the rapidly growing mound of nappies, prepared the dinner and looked forward to the afternoon walk. She had convinced herself she was happy with her lot, and yet felt disappointed at the pangs of jealousy endured on hearing of a friend's glamorous job or another's academic and erudite husband. If only someone noticed her from time to time, or even wrote her name on a wall declaring her existence worthwhile; 'A fine mind' or 'I was once her lover'. That way, at least, she would have evidence she was having impact on others. As it was, she was perpetually bombarded with it. Marital successes, even marital failures evoked a response from her. All one-way traffic.

That afternoon she dressed the baby and started out for her walk. 'Fantasy time' her husband called it. 'Wall-reading time' she knew it to be. On this occasion, how-ever, she decided to avoid those concrete temptations and, instead, visit the park. Out along the main road she trundled, pushing the pram, pausing to gaze into the hardware store's window, hearing the whine of the Sara-cen as it thundered by, waking the baby and making her feel uneasy. A foot patrol of soldiers strolled past, their rifles, lethal even in the brittle sunlight of this March day, lounged lovingly and relaxed in the arms of their men. One soldier stood nonchalantly, almost impertinent, against a corrugated railing and stared at her. She always blushed on passing troops.

The park is ugly, stark and hostile. Even in summer, when courting couples seek out secluded spots like mating cats, they reject Musgrave. There are a few trees, clustered together, standing like skeletons, ashamed of their nakedness. The rest is grass, a green wasteland speckled with puddles of gulls squawking over a worm patch. The park is bordered by a hospital with a military wing which is guarded by an army billet. The beauty of the place, it has only this, is its silence.

The hill up to the park bench was not the precipice it seemed, but the baby and pram were heavy. Ante-natal self-indulgence had taken its toll – her midriff was now most definitely a bulge. With one final push, pram, baby and mother reached the green wooden seat, and came to rest. The baby slept soundly with the soother touching her velvet pink cheeks, hand on pillow, a picture of purity. The woman heard a coughing noise coming from the nearby gun turret, and managed to see the tip of a rifle and a face peering out from the darkness. Smells of cabbage and burnt potatoes wafted over from behind the slanting sheets of protective steel.

'Is that your baby?' an English voice called out. She could barely see the face belonging to the voice. She replied yes, and smiled. The situation reminded her of the confessional. Dark and supposedly anonymous, 'Is that you, my child?' She knew the priest personally. Did he identify her sins with his 'Good morning, Mary,' and think to himself, 'and I know what you were up to last night!' She blushed at the secrets given away during the ceremony. Yes, she nervously answered again, it was her baby, a little girl. First-time mothers rarely resist the temptation to talk about their offspring. Forgetting her initial shyness, she told the voice of when the baby was born, the early problems of all-night crying, now teething, how she could crawl backwards and gurgle.

The voice responded. It too had a son, a few months

84

older than her child, away in Germany at the army base at Munster. Factory pipes, chimney tops, church spires, domes all listened impassively to the Englishman's declaration of paternal love. The scene was strange, for although Belfast's sterile geography slipped into classical forms with dusk and heavy rain-clouds, the voice and the woman knew the folly of such innocent communication. They politely finished their conversation, said goodbye, and the woman pushed her pram homewards. The voice remained in the turret, watchful and anxious. Home she went, past vanloads of workers leering out at the pavement, past the uneasy presence of foot patrols, past the church.'Let us give each other the sign of peace,' they said at Mass. The only sign Belfast knew was two fingers pointing towards Heaven. Life was self-contained, the couple often declared, just like flats. No need to go outside.

She did go outside, however. Each week the voice and the woman learned more of each other. No physical contact was needed, no face-to-face encounter to judge reaction, no touching to confirm amity, no threat of dangerous intimacy. It was a meeting of minds, as she explained later to her husband, a new opinion, a common bond, an opening of vistas. He disclosed his ambitions to become a pilot, to watching the land, fields and horizons spread out beneath him – a patchwork quilt of dappled colours and textures. She wanted to be remembered by writing on walls, about them that is, a world-shattering thesis on their psychological complexities, their essential truths, their witticisms and intellectual genius. And all this time the city's skyline and distant buildings watched and listened.

It was April now. More slogans had appeared, white and dripping, on the city walls. 'Brits out. Peace in.' A simple equation for the writer. 'Loose talk claims lives', another shouted menacingly. The messages, the woman decided, had acquired a more ominous tone. The baby had grown and could sit up without support. New political solutions had been proposed and rejected, inter-paramilitary feuding had broken out and subsided, four soldiers and two policemen had been blown to smithereens in separate incidents, and a building a day had been bombed by the Provos. It had been a fairly normal month by Belfast's standards. The level of violence was no more or less acceptable than at other times.

One day – it was, perhaps, the last day in April – her husband returned home panting and trembling a little. He asked had she been to the park, and she replied she had. Taking her by the hand, he led her to the wall on the left of their driveway. She felt her heart sink and thud against her. She felt her face redden. Her mouth was suddenly dry. She could not speak. In huge angry letters the message spat itself out,

'TOUT'.

The four-letter word covered the whole wall. It clanged in her brain, its venom rushed through her body. Suspicion was enough to condemn. The job itself was not well done, she had seen better. The letters were uneven, paint splattered down from the cross T, the U looked a misshapen O. The workmanship was poor, the impact perfect.

Her husband led her back into the kitchen. The baby was crying loudly in the livingroom but the woman did not seem to hear. Like sleepwalkers, they sat down on the settee. The woman began to sob. Her shoulders heaved in bursts as she gasped hysterically. Her husband took her in his arms gently and tried to make her sorrow his. Already he shared her fear.

'What did you talk about? Did you not realise how dangerous it was? We must leave.' He spoke quickly, making plans. Selling the house and car, finding a job in London or Dublin, far away from Belfast, mortgages, removals, savings, the tawdry affairs of normal living stunned her, making her more confused. 'I told him nothing,' she sobbed, 'what could I tell? We talked about life, everything, but not about here.' She trembled, trying to control herself. 'We just chatted about reading walls, families, anything at all. Oh Sean, it was as innocent as that. A meeting of minds we called it, for it was little else.'

She looked into her husband's face and saw he did not fully understand. There was a hint of jealousy, of resentment at not being part of their communication. Her hands fell on her lap, resting in resignation. What was the point of explanation? She lifted her baby from the floor. Pressing the tiny face and body to her breast, she felt all her hopes and desires for a better life become one with the child's struggle for freedom. The child's hands wandered over her face, their eyes met. At once that moment of maternal and filial love eclipsed her fear, gave her the impetus to escape.

For nine months she had been unable to accept the reality of her condition. Absurd, for the massive bump daily shifted position and thumped against her. When her daughter was born, she had been overwhelmed by love for her and amazed at her own ability to give life. By nature she was a dreamy person, given to moments of fancy. She wondered at her competence in fulfilling the role of mother. Could it be measured? This time she knew it could. She really did not care if they maimed her or even murdered her. She did care about her daughter. She was her touchstone, her anchor to virtue. Not for her child a legacy of fear, revulsion or hatred. With the few hours respite the painters had left between judgement and sentence she determined to leave Belfast's walls behind.

The next few nights were spent in troubled, restless sleep. The message remained on the wall outside. The neighbours pretended not to notice and refused to discuss the matter. She and the baby remained indoors despite the refreshing May breezes and blue skies. Her husband had given in his notice at the office, for health reasons, he suggested to his colleagues. An aunt had been contacted in Dublin. The couple did not answer knocks at the door. They carefully examined the shape and size of mail delivered and always paused when they answered the telephone.

The mini-van was to call at eleven on Monday night,

when it would be dark enough to park, and pack their belongings and themselves without too much suspicion being aroused. The firm had been very understanding when the nature of their work had been explained. They were Protestant so there was no conflict of loyalties involved in the exercise. They agreed to drive them to Dublin at extra cost, changing drivers at Newry on the way down.

Monday finally arrived. The couple nervously laughed about how smoothly everything had gone. Privately, they each expected something to go wrong. The baby was fed, and played with, the radio listened to and the clock watched. They listened to the news at nine. Huddled together in their anxiety, they kept vigil in the darkening room. Rain had begun to pour from black thunderclouds. Everywhere it was quiet and still. Hushed and cold they waited. Ten o'clock, and it was now dark. A blustery wind had risen, making the lattice separation next door bang and clatter. At ten to eleven, her husband went into the sitting-room to watch for the mini-van. His footsteps clamped noisily on the floorboards as he paced back and forth. The baby slept.

A black shape glided slowly up the street and backed into the driveway. It was eleven. The van had arrived. Her husband asked to see their identification and then they began to load up the couple's belongings. Settee, chairs, television, washing machine – all were dumped hastily, it was no time to worry about breakages. She stood holding the sleeping baby in the living-room as the men worked anxiously between van and house. The scene was so unreal, the circumstances absolutely incredible. She thought, 'What have I done?' Recollections of her naivety, her insensibility to historical fact and political climate were stupifying. She had seen women who had been tarred and feathered, heard of people who had been shot in the head, boys who had been knee-capped, all for suspected fraternising with troops. The catalogue of violence spilled out before her as she realised the gravity and possible repercussions of her alleged misdemeanour.

88

A voice called her, 'Mary, come on now. We have to go. Don't worry, we're all together.' Her husband led her to the locked and waiting van. Handing the baby to him, she climbed up beside the driver, took back the baby as her husband sat down beside her and waited for the engine to start. The van slowly manoeuvred out onto the street and down the main road. They felt more cheerful now, a little like refugees seeking safety and freedom not too far away. As they approached the motorway bridge, two figures with something clutched in their hands stood side by side in the darkness. She closed her eyes tightly, expecting bursts of gunfire. The van shot past. Relieved, she asked her husband what they were doing at this time of night. 'Writing slogans on the wall,' he replied.

The furtiveness of the painters seemed ludicrous and petty as she recalled the heroic and literary characteristics with which she had endowed them. What did they matter? The travellers sat in silence as the van sped past the city suburbs, the glare of police and army barracks, on out and further out into the countryside. Past sleeping villages and silent fields, past whitewashed farmhouses and barking dogs. On to Newry where they said goodbye to their driver as the new one stepped in. Far along the coast with Rostrevor's twinkling lights opposite the bay down to the Border check and a drowsy soldier waving them through. Out of the North, safe, relieved and heading for Dublin.

Some days later in Belfast the neighbours discovered the house vacant, the people next door received a letter and a cheque from Dublin. Remarks about the peculiar couple were made over hedges and cups of coffee. the message on the wall was painted over by the couple who had bought the house when it went up for sale. They too were ordinary people, living a self-contained life, worrying over finance and babies, promotion and local gossip. He too had an office job, but his

wife was merely a housekeeper for him. She was sens-
ible, down to earth, and not in the least inclined to
wall-reading.

*Winner of the Maxwell House Women Writers' Compet-
ition 1979 and first published by Arlen House.*

Snipers

Ann W. Gleave

Yesterday
in thick crumples of
sickness and sad recollection
I opened the lid
of the box of despair
and much more
than ever I had witnessed
opened a slow eye.
I saw that my own tears
were as dew
for snowdrops in moss.
For me
the kitten's bright eyes
came through a raging night
when all seemed lost,
for me
he ran
lightning again
down the hall
and his mother
stretched by the fire.
For me
winter's choking dark
changed to
breath of gold
in a day
and the old cat
sat out in sunlight again
blinking his tired eyes.
For me
the riches
and crowded colours
of life and greeting
passed
much as they always do,
unproclaimed
and
unremarkable

as roses.

The box
I was rash enough to open
lies there even now,
I know,
containing its
poisonous breath
waiting
in case I should
fail to recall
the surety
of that which now I sing:
the rebirth
that is your dark eye.

For within the box
in canister
in sinister quiet
are
surgical wards
and the blood red stain,
cattle trucks,
prisons,
derelict mismarriage of
war and peace,
orphans,
victims of flood and fire.
The knives,
the implements,
the ash grey cloud
borne on a silver wing,
the sniper's foothold
on earth,
pushing
pushing at the lock.

I should wear poppies
every day
lest I forget.

Happy Birth Day

Brenda Murphy

I had bitten Adam's apple, now I was bearing the fruit.

'Push, push!' they said. 'That's it, you're doing fine... Now don't push.
Pant, pant!'

I want to scream – maybe it will shatter the pain open – but I must not.

I must push again, I must push, now push this constricting lump out of my body. I want it out. At this moment it is not a baby, it is a pain I want to get rid of. I feel it will rip open the seams of my skin. I will burst like some human tomato. This child is holding onto my womb, clutching my flesh in its tiny fists like bits of material. It's coming out, but it's taking my insides with it.

I am consumed now by the urge to push and eject. It slides out and they lift it from between my legs and they hand me a bloody, purple-faced child with a husky cry and trembling, tiny hands. I take it – it's a girl. I put her to my breast and feel the tingle of soft sucks. I touch the matted hair, plastered down on her head with my blood.

I fall in love. It has caught me unawares. I did not think I could feel this, would feel this. A blood-stained, purple-faced little bastard and I love her instantly.

Under Control

Mary Beckett

Thursday.

My Dear Peggy,

Why do I burden you with this? I remember when Mother told me about her worries I used to say to myself, 'Why does she pile it all on me? What's wrong with her talking to Father?' I normally talk things over with Owen, you know that, but when I see the looks of dislike that he gives his beloved daughter nowadays, I can't say a word to him about her. I know you love her and will be able to separate fact from fiction in what I tell you. And she loves you far more than she does me. 'Do you know how much I hate you?' she asked me this morning. It was no shock to me but I didn't like to hear it said. I told her I knew she didn't like me and that it was a pity because I loved her, always loved her, that she was especially dear to me being our first baby after the little one that died. She told me then that I was telling lies, that I never thought much of her but that I'd hated her since before Susan was born.

Did Stella ever tell you how she came to have the baby? She's fond of you and must be grateful to you – maybe she told you before now what she told me this morning. 'Told' is not a proper verb to describe her onslaught on me. She was shouting – yelling, until I warned her she'd waken Susan. All the time she looked at me with such detestation that I have to off-load it. It's hard for me at this moment to remember the quiet polite girl Stella was all through school, no trouble to anyone and the nuns always telling me she was responsible and co-operative and that it didn't matter at all that her exam results were very mediocre. I used to think she was content – happy would be too strong a word. She didn't go out much, no dances, no boy-friends. I hoped going to the university would improve that but she just stayed with her school-friends and worried about her notes and

94

her exams and her money. She was anxious to get a summer job so as to have her own money for the next year and when she got one in a kind of youth hostel in France we were all delighted. I thought it would help her French. She tells me now that I pushed her into taking it just to improve her French, that she was terrified of going and that she was killed with loneliness while she was there and what she really wanted was to get into a shop or an office here at home. Her wicked mother threw her out of the nest and she hadn't spoken to a soul all the fortnight she was there before the Friday she telephoned us to find out if she had passed her first year exam. She hadn't, you remember. Owen had gone over to the university and found that her name was not on the list of passes, but we didn't know how many subjects she had failed and wouldn't until Monday, so we hadn't rung her and hoped she wouldn't ring us but she did, after dinnertime, and I had to tell her. I remember consoling her with the assurance that she'd get her repeat exam in September, that she should stay where she was until she heard how many subjects she had to repeat.

This morning she said that I ordered her to stay where she was, that she'd just have to pass in September or she wouldn't be acceptable at home. She wanted to give up university she says. She never wanted to go to university. She didn't enjoy studying. She was never any good at it. She hated not doing well in exams when Brian and David were so clever. All she wanted was to get a job and enjoy her own money and her freedom from books. But I was so determined to control her, to push her into things she had no wish for, that she had no chance to run her own life, so she just had the baby force some change.

She had gone into the nearest town just before dark because she was too depressed to stay in her room. By a strange chance she met a lad she'd known to see in College, but not to speak to. He was cock-a-hoop because he had passed his final law exams and since he had nobody to celebrate with they went off together and ended up in his bed. When she went back to the hostel she scrubbed herself all over in disgust – every place he had touched, her teeth, her tongue, in horror at herself. Still, on Monday after she rang home and found out she had failed only French and I was insistent that she'd have no difficulty passing one subject in September, the only way out she could think of was to go back to this lad every evening for a week until he moved off to Switzerland. Now, you may think this was confiding in me, but not if you'd heard her. It was as if I had arranged for her violation.

I had never allowed myself to wonder how or when it happened. That would have been like reading a diary or her letters. Owen used to say many a time before the baby was born, 'Did she ever tell you how she came to do such a thing?' and I always said no but that I supposed it was because of loneliness, human nature and the skimpy clothes they wore in the heat. They certainly were not in love although maybe Stella was a bit dazzled by him. When she told him in September that she was pregnant he said he took no responsibility, that he was going on for the bar, and could have no blemish on his character, and if she said anything he'd deny ever having spoken to her in his life. But you know that. It's all very well for her to say now that she deliberately decided to change her life, but I remember the pathetic picture she made when she told me just afterwards. She didn't know what to do, so it was as well I did, in spite of all her talk of my being so domineering. And of course we couldn't have managed if you hadn't been living in England and prepared to take her until after the baby was born. How does any woman manage without a sister? I sometimes feel if our first baby had lived she would have made a difference to Stella. She could have confided in a sister earlier about her irritation with me and her rancour might not have grown into this hatred she feels for me now. She tells me that by making her keep the baby a secret from her brothers I have cut her off from them. But she never was close to Brian and David, and Patrick always loved her. He told me while she was away with you that he missed her because he loved her more than anybody in the world, more than me or his father. Now she takes no notice of him. Granted he's two years older and not a cuddly little boy any more, but he tells her jokes and she won't laugh and he asks her riddles and she doesn't answer. I feel like shaking her.

What should I have done when she told me she was pregnant? That's what I asked her this morning. I thought we were doing the best we could in saying she was taking a year away from the university to work in a bookshop in Oxford and live with you and Terence and give a hand with your children. I know there were raised eyebrows round here when she didn't come home for Christmas but I said, 'You know what they're like at that age – they do what they feel like at the moment.' After that I began to tell people we were planning to adopt a baby due to be born in March to a girl Stella had met in Oxford. I used to have to try and get Owen to stop looking so gloomy and bowed. It aged him ten years – it really did. I'd waken in the morning seeing blue skies and then I'd remember about Stella over with you, waiting for her baby without a husband to comfort her or me to mind her, and while I was washing my face I'd cry into the wash-basin and dry away the tears with the towel because I daren't let anybody see me in that state.

I don't want to boss people about or control their lives, but I have never found anybody else prepared to make the decisions. I've been aware of my bossiness for a long time – since just before I left school. I never told anybody at home but I decided then that I had better be a nun. I was miserable at boarding-school, homesick from morning to night, hating the way every minute was in some timetable. That's why, after me, you were made to travel to school by bike and bus, getting soaked as often as not and constantly complaining about the activities you missed. The only time I was happy was in the Chapel. You remember the Chapel – all soaring white, and our September miseries ambered by the sun through the west window while we sang the Magnificat, our voices high and pure in the very controlled plain chant. Someone told me that my red hair under the black mantilla looked beautiful in that light. I treasured the compliment. I thought if I could stay there on my knees and say 'Here I am Lord,' He would reach down His hand and I would reach up mine (figuratively of course) and I could reflect His beauty and order in a pool of sunshine all the rest of my life. So I went to Sr. Ambrose and told her I was thinking of becoming a nun, and she said, 'Now Kathleen you will have to give that serious thought. We'll leave it to God's will but I myself think you are quite unsuited to community life. You must realise you have not settled happily at all during the six years you have been with us.' I told her I knew that but I was prepared to offer that up and she said, oh very drily, 'I imagine it would be an uncomfortable position for the Sisters – being offered up. The truth is, Kathleen, that you never come into any group without directing them what to do and how to do it.' I just gasped a couple of times and went out of the room.

I had never noticed it in myself but I tried to stop it and more or less managed until I got married but my God, Peggy, if I didn't tell everybody what to do here they would all just drift. I keep wishing they had plans of their own, for jobs or holidays or anything. I keep hoping when they don't mention anything they have secret ideas, but no. At the last minute I am asked 'What do *you* think I should do?' I didn't force Stella into the university. We repeatedly asked her what she wanted to do and she shrugged or muttered that she didn't know and took herself off to her room. I thought an arts degree would be no burden to her but we didn't make her do it – it costs us plenty. We promised ourselves never to mention how little we can afford it, although sometimes nowadays Owen begins to growl about it to Brian and David. When he catches my eye he stops. Isn't it a strange thing that she's passed every exam since then, only it doesn't seem to lift her heart at all. She sits her finals in a couple of months and then she'll be finished with study if she wants to be. There is nothing to prevent her getting a job, untrammelled, meeting people, living whatever kind of life she makes for herself. She says that by keeping Susan in the house I will never let her forget what she's been through. I don't know what to think.

Is she telling me the real truth in this version of Susan's conception or is she dressing up her weakness in the guise of decision, knowing how I laud decisiveness and deplore its lack? Or does she care what I approve of? She does hate me. If she had only glared hatred I could have told myself she was in bad form or overworked and that anyway she is not at her best in the mornings. But she put it into words and I'll not be able to forget it. She never used to sit around like this in the mornings. Did she do it in your house? When she came home I didn't like to say anything because I thought she needed extra consideration and gentleness. While I'm dressing and feeding Susan she sits there, shows no interest, doesn't smile when Susan chuckles or chatters. She blights our enjoyment of that part of the day. She tells me now that she hates the clothes I put on Susan, trousers or dungarees and jerseys, unchanged since she herself was that age. There are frilly old-world dresses she says would suit Susan beautifully and would show she belongs to a different generation. But Susan goes out to play with all the children on the road and she would not be comfortable or indeed warm enough in pretty dresses. She is the loveliest, happiest child, Peggy, mischievous and energetic. Stella says I make a fool of myself running after her, that I am too old and too stout and that if I'm going to bend over on the footpath to lift up a struggling child I should wear tights and not stockings. Oh she can mortify me with her tongue. I felt the same shame I used to feel on the hockey field when Sister Reginald used to shout 'Spaces, Kathleen!' and it was nothing to do with the game but with a bit of leg escaped between black stockings and navy knickers.

I hope your children never wound you, Peggy. Yours are younger of course but oh dear do be careful never to make them your enemies. You have an advantage over me in that you are affectionate and demonstrative. Why are we so different, both reared the same way? I'd like to blame the boarding school but I can't honestly believe that I would be any more prone to hugging and kissing if I had stayed at home. Once the children are as tall as I am I no longer touch them, nor they me. I love to look at them and listen to them and think about them but I don't touch them. Patrick will soon be out of my reach. That's why Susan is such a bonus to me.

Do you remember when I went over to bring her home? I behaved very badly and you were mad with me. I've been sorry ever since but then I could act in no other way. All I could think of was to separate Stella from the baby so that nobody could connect them in their minds, your children, your Terence, your neighbours, even though they knew, they wouldn't think in the future of the baby being anything to do with Stella if I whisked her away quickly and left Stella behind until the end of the summer. Terence wanted to show me Oxford and I wish now I had seen it properly because when will I have the chance again. All I have is a confused impression of sulphur-coloured colleges in a murky mist of rain and boated bends of river swelling quietly in fields the way no Irish river ever did. I am glad your beautiful house stands on a hill. Next time I come I will be relaxed and enjoy your company and your affluence and I won't be always on my feet with anxiety to catch the plane. Stella says I never looked at her in the hospital and it could well be true. On the plane back with the little unknown baby on my knee I thought the best thing would be for the aeroplane to fall out of the sky, through the clouds, and we'd all be dead before we hit the ground. Rather the baby and I would be dead, never mind the other passengers, and our troubles would be over, hers and mine and Stella's too. Then I remembered Patrick at home aged eight and I hadn't even a present for him. Sure enough when I got out of the taxi there he was on his own because Brian and David had taken themselves off hostelling in Kerry as soon as I was gone and Owen had gone to work having asked Maura next door to keep an eye on him, that he'd be all right. He burst into tears when he saw me he was so relieved but for ages afterwards he kept on asking me what did I need a baby for. I think he has always resented losing his place as the youngest.

Owen complained about losing his sleep with a new baby wakening up in the night and he doesn't like still having the cot in our room. There is no bedroom for Susan and he suggests putting her in with Stella. I can't do that the way things are. I used to examine Susan for resemblances to Stella. I had my answer ready for any neighbour who would see some hint. I would point out that the butcher's wife adopted two little girls who grew not only to resemble her but each other. The only family sign I could see in Susan is the way her curls grow out in circles from the crown of her head exactly the same as the white waves on my mother-in-law. But she is old and living in Kilkenny and nobody else saw it, not even Owen, but he doesn't look at Susan the way he looked at his own. There's something a bit primitive about him that he balks at bringing up another man's child. But I love her. I love the bright intelligent way she has of looking at me as if I always know what she has in her mind. I never enjoyed my other children. At least that's the way it seems to me looking back. They came too close together, except Patrick, and I was tired and bothered and haunted by the death of our first baby. That knocked all the confidence out of me. I stopped being young then. Only Owen has any idea. Now I think I could bear anything in the world so long as Susan is well and happy. I waken up in the night sometimes in terror that she'd get sick or be killed in an accident and I have to get up and look at her in her cot.

If Stella is unhappy living in this house she can move out to a flat once she's in a job and Susan can have her room. Or we can build an extension when we scrape up the money. It will be for Stella to choose. I will never refer again to her outburst of this morning. That's why I'm getting it off my chest to you. I don't expect you to make any answer to all of this. Don't worry. Everything is again under control.

I will write in a day or two an ordinary letter and ask about Terence, and your children in their international school and why your children and mine and those of my neighbours have always walked on walls and shouted on Sundays while English children never do. Are we such savages? Isn't it a pity you can't relax on a holiday at home, where they could run through fields and play in barns. But our own brother having got the place has no welcome for either of us. When I have time to think of it I resent that our families are reduced to concrete, cut off by him from where we were reared. That's an exaggeration; it's probably all an exaggeration – the whole letter.

Love,

Kathleen.

Change of Life

Evelyn Berman

I think I'll be leaving now, he says
I've had quite a lot of education
And I'm feeling pretty fit
I think I can manage on my own now.

It can't be time for you to go, I say
You can hardly tie your shoes
Only the other week you fell
Trying to walk a fence top
We had to go to the hospital to have your hand stitched
I remember.

Mother, that was years ago, he says
Really, I must be off.

I want to say, Please don't go
You are my last child
When you go the house will be silent
No one will climb over the landing banisters
And jump down into the hall
Or pretend to strangle in the bead curtain
No one will come to visit with toothbrush in breast
            pocket
And six tapes of loud music for luggage
I shall walk round empty tidy bedrooms
And choose all the television programmes
I shall probably never know what's number one in the
            charts.

But I don't say anything, and he's relieved that I'm
            taking it so well.

I'll write to you often, he says
And telephone, and there'll be the holidays
I'll never forget you, you can be sure.

He probably won't forget me
He may even mention me at times to people who don't
      know me
Whom I don't know
Tell them some anecdote of family life
And they will nod and smile and talk of other things.

Circus Love

Delia Rimington

The Bearded Lady fell in love
With the man who kept the seals.
She followed him where'er he went,
Washed for him, cooked his meals.
One day the circus came to rest
Upon the village green.
The Seal Man saw the village Belle,
She was sweet sixteen.
The Bearded Lady thought a lot,
What could she do about it?
And finally she shaved her beard
And confronted him without it.
The Seal Man taken by surprise,
His laughter came in peals.
He said he did not like her face
He'd rather have his seals.
The Bearded Lady walked away,
That generous hirsute giver.
Next day as dawn was breaking,
They found her in the river.

The Palm House

Shirley Bork

I park the car on a yellow dotted line. Being ignorant of
traffic regulations, I just hope that I won't collect a
ticket. The uneasy feeling persists until I pass through
the gates into the Botanic Gardens, then I forget, partly
anyway. It's a crisp autumn morning and I'm walking
towards the university pretending to myself that I'm a
student. There is still enough heat in the sun to encourage strolling. The piles of leaves, swept from the
lawns in front of the museum, smell bitter and nostalgic.

A girl comes towards me along the path. She has a
fresh, open face, smiling. Her shoulder-length hair flows
as she walks with a confident stride. I don't look a
convincing student at all. My face has a bewildered
expression. Was it because I spent the long drive into
town thinking about you? No matter how I chew the
problem over it never comes to any solution. The thing
you suggested was so radical – and you admitted as much
– that it would take some getting used to, however
liberal I might consider myself.

I pass the concrete cliff of the museum and the beds
of pink roses, out through the gates into University
Road. Students flow up and down in a jean-clad tide. Do
I blend? I wish I was a stone lighter. It's only conceit for
someone my age to wear jeans, but I don't feel old and
certainly don't look like the tweed-suited, silk-scarved
ladies heading for the Extra-Mural Department. They
look as though they had come straight from the hair-
dresser's and been dropped off at the gates by husbands
in expensive cars. I can't identify with them but follow
them nonetheless.

I check that your letter is still in my pocket. What
would all these well-bred ladies make of a man like you?
A man who can casually suggest that the solution to our
problem is for the three of us to live together. You said,

'I can't let Helen down.' And I don't want you to. But how can it work in practice? How will she feel about it? I'm on the outside. If I want you it has to be a share but she has a right to expect the whole of you. You have both given up a lot to be together.

Well, perhaps in a couple of hours I'll know. I wonder why you said 'Meet me in the Palm House'. Echoes of *Last Year at Marienbad*? Do you need a surrealist setting for the strange conversation we are likely to have? And have you thought about her kids and your kids and mine?

I wait outside the Palm House. A compound fracture of scaffolding rips through the delicate skin of glass. Bits of leafy metalwork which form a border to the roof just above head level are more absent than present. The building is only a sketch of itself. A sketch from which a Palm House could be built but which no longer exists. The few remaining palms look sad and neglected. The only life inside is the constant coming and going of sparrows who can't read the notice – 'DANGER KEEP OUT'. How can we meet inside? Oh well, it's a warm, bench-sitting afternoon. You can't miss me if I sit here.

Two soldiers stand just inside the park gates. They are scarcely more than boys. A wisp of an old lady coming into the park solemnly presents each of them with an ice lolly and without a word scuttles on. They may, after all, have some good memories of Belfast.

A man walks along with his son, the boy's hand on his shoulder in a gesture reminiscent of gassed soldiers in the First World War. The boy isn't blind. He has the stiff, frightened gait of the brain-damaged. He is about eighteen years old, very brown and fit-looking, but his hair is cut in an unsympathetic, institutional style that would have suited a twelve year-old in the thirties.

I know this man's life. I know how it feels to go cold as the doctor with the bland expression says, as you know he was going to, 'I'm sorry, we can't do any more for him. It's remarkable the way they sometimes improve, but I'm not offering you too much hope. He may never be able to do much more for himself than he can do now. You understand our position. We're so short of beds... You're young. You can always have another child. It's unlikely to happen again.'

'Thank you, I do understand.' I collect my baby from his tiny ward. I haven't seen him for three weeks. There is no visiting in the baby ward.

'He wouldn't know you, dear. It isn't the same as an older child, is it? And think of all the germs the visitors bring in. Your baby's very sick.'

The Sister may have meant well, but in my agony I wanted to scream – 'He's MY baby! I want to see him!'

Now I was seeing him. Surely this can't be the right bed. My baby looks like a Botticelli angel. He wasn't really ill, just wouldn't wake for his feed. Now this! The swollen head, the blue rings round the eyes which flick constantly from side to side, the slack skin and the stick-like limbs of the Oxfam poster.

'Just take him home and love him.' And play him all the symphonies he'll never understand; and walk with him in the park when he's eighteen as this man does with his son, and watch him smile at the people and the flowers with equal recognition.

I wish I could walk along with this man, this boy. I know this life. But I have to wait here for you, on this bench in the sun.

There are a lot of old people meandering in the Gardens this afternoon. They all seem to wear hats and carry the same two-handled, zip-topped shopping bag. Almost as though they had been issued along with their pension book. The contents are standard too: knitting, library book to be changed, nylon mac rolled up tight and secured with rubber band and the inevitable food supply. Consumers to the end... I dread being old. And you being old. And none of us knowing the other is to die. They all go on eating and sleeping and watching telly and getting older and pretending they're not going to die. Don't they know they're dying?

Where are you?

I won't keep looking at the gates, the path along which you might come. My eyes are blurred with staring anyway. A bright light worms in the centre of my vision. The passing faces all have their right eye missing. I'll read my book. Then when you come I'll glance at your shoes standing beside me and see your legs and the little white paint stain just below the knee of your jeans. The stain always reminds me that when you moved in together it was to be just the two of you. Helen chose the house. You decorated it. Together. You scrubbed the floors and put up the pictures. Now here *I* am, coming from your past. From a time before you knew her. Coming from a time when we all had partners and homes and children in a neat, orderly pattern.

How I wish you would come. Explain it all to me again. Make me understand, like a kind uncle explaining, saying, 'Look at me when I'm talking to you,' in your half-bulying way. How can I say that to look at you confuses me utterly? I can only listen when I'm *not* looking.

I wonder if I worry the soldiers keeping guard behind the gatepost? Perhaps I should tell them that there is nothing suspicious in my sitting here, constantly glancing in their direction and writing in a notebook. I wish it was summer and the park was full of teenage lovers and dogs and babies in prams. It didn't feel foolish then to meet and stroll along hand in hand as though the park made us invisible. I felt seventeen. The rest of the world didn't exist.

Please come. Please don't let me sit here getting more and more confused. I can't be in the wrong place. There is only one Palm House, it's quite famous. You can't have meant the other glasshouse further up. In any case surely you would have looked for me wherever I was. I must wait here, be patient. But please, please come.

Have you ever sat in the park on a sunny autumn day, crying? It isn't just that you don't come but the park is a very sad place. All these down-and-outs waiting for

109

the shelter to open, all these old people and cripples, lonely and lost. Can any of them be as lonely as I am?

A little boy comes up to me and, shading his eyes with his ice-cream cornet, stares up into my face. Then, having decided that he was right, wanders off again.

A woman in a flowered hat gives me a sideways look as she passes, then resumes her conversation. 'Oh, you can get a lovely cup of tea in the museum. Nice cakes, just like home-made. I hate that factory stuff.' When she gets to the far end of the lawn she turns right round to have another look.

You can't have meant to be so cruel. When I get home there will be a letter waiting for me. A message. You will explain. It will be all right. You did mean what you said. I'll just look at the gates once more, then I'll go. You won't come now.

The woman in the flowered hat comes back with a policeman. He is solicitous and concerned, but he isn't going to understand. Is it an offence to cry in a public place? Could it be classed as 'Disturbing the peace'? I shall never be able to tell them that I'm crying for all the people in the park. Not just that someone didn't turn up.

Others round me now. Talking to each other. Talking AT me. I can't understand what they mean. The sun still feels warm on my skin. It must be nearly three. The sky reflects off the Palm House roof. This isn't me. It's all happening to a rather pathetic, middle-aged woman. Someone I don't recognise.

Now, at last, here is someone I know. Helen will explain why I'm crying. It will be all right; the three of us.

'I'm a friend of hers, officer. I'll take her for a cup of tea, she'll feel better then.' She leans down, her face close to mine, and takes my arm. 'Sheila, will you come?'

She is very beautiful and generous and vulnerable. I begin to understand.

'Yes. We'll have a cup of tea. They do a lovely cup of tea in the museum.'

110

Exile

(my mentally handicapped son)

Mary Twomey

It was not what I had expected overnight
In my stencilled garden.
This sudden pungent rain forest plant
Exiled from jungle or orangery
Or at least a glass house.
Cautiously I approached
Peeled back protective leaves
To look inside the improbable chalice flower
Curved upwards towards me.
I touched and
Yes, I said yes
For questions were being asked.
Now I too am outside the pale
While watchful undecided eyes
Consider me.
As I tend this singular species
I seek definition
Crave for a kind of justice
I am Munch's 'Silent Scream' for assimilation.

Documentary

Mary McGowan

A bedspring squeaks
An ear pricks
A mind ticks
And records –
Marriage consummation
For mass consumption.

Inner City

Francine Cunningham

My head hurts.

Somewhere in the city
a man is gaping,
his walnut brain
cracked open.

I feel a need for the surreal –

the sharp, sensual shock
as I bite through the easy
flesh of an over-ripe strawberry
on a dank Belfast street.

A Riot

Anne Noble

Every dog has his day. It was the day of the Ulster Workers' Council Strike.

'We've got the support of the people... we'll fight for our rights and die for them if necessary. Our people are behind us one hundred per cent... this is a fight to the finish! Everyone is behind us, everyone behind us to a man. Intimidation? ...Nonsense... Who said there was intimidation? We only used clubs to encourage them to stay at home. The people knew their duty. Petrol! ...What would they want with petrol when they had no wish to go to work? Interference with the bread and milk deliveries? ...More propaganda, exaggeration! – we allowed a certain amount of milk and bread through... and didn't we allow the shops to open for a few hours each day? Hardship for the farmers? ...A load of rot... they were behind us all the way... right up to the hilt. You saw them on television, you heard them... willing to lose homes, farms, animals and machinery... the lot... even said they'd eat grass if necessary. You can't argue with that now... it's plain and straight for you. This is it... it's do or die now... it's a fight to the finish.'

There were widespread reports of intimidation as some tried to go to work.

'Blacklegs, turncoats, Lundys,' men and women shrieked as white-faced office girls hurried past them.

Margaret Caldwell shrank as a woman disengaged herself and caught her by the collar of her coat.

'Hey you... remember 1690,' she screeched.

'If you're not for us you're against us,' a voice snarled from the crowd.

A police van cruised by as Margaret rushed towards the office.

Mr Green, the office manager, was disturbed. It would not be worth it, they could break in and wreck the

113

place. Play it cool, he decided. Give the hotheads a chance to cool down. A few days and everything would be back to normal. He let them out the back door and told them to report for work the following week.

There were no shops open, crowds roamed the streets, the general mood was menacing, dangerous... waiting...

Margaret walked home. A police van preceded a blaring ambulance siren... more wailing sirens... another ambulance... the noise was deafening... A young woman stood staring... staring... transfixed. she put a hand to her brow, sobbed noisily, and hid in a doorway. There was a demonstration going on at the Square. Margaret could hear the shrill, vicious sounds. Evil vibrations... a sort of insanity. Bloody nutballs! Rabble! Mindless rabble! And they looked like any other human being.

'They're handing in a protest at the police station at the Pass. It's about the detention of our men,' a man informed her.

She hurried home to her two teenage children... poor teenagers Sharon and Peter... their adolescent problems merging into the imbalance and confusion around them.

'You were silly going into your work. I told you, you shouldn't go,' Peter greeted her. 'They'd attack you in a minute, we were watching them from the front window. They were walking up and down to see if any of the shops were open... some tough-looking nuts among them, I can tell you.'

'We'll have to queue up to get some bread and milk when they allow the shops to open for a couple of hours after lunch,' Sharon said. 'I bet the people who started all this don't have to queue for their stuff. I'm sure it wouldn't last long if they had to suffer.'

The strike continued. No trains between Dublin and Belfast, no Heysham or Liverpool steamers leaving the docks. A complete blockade. No letters, no telegrams except on matters of life and death, and now the increased threat of no gas and electricity in the immediate future. 'Meat could run out tomorrow... Crippled firms put hundreds on the dole... Petrol only for essential services,' the headlines read... no papers next!

God save us from this tide of insanity. Men dressed in paramilitary uniforms checking drivers' credentials. Women and children linking arms to prevent people trying to get to their work... and now talk of ration cards... they say they're already on issue in East Belfast. It's complete isolation from civilised people. It'll be a return to the days of the famine, and what did the English care then? ...Victoria cavorting over the hills and dales with John Brown while the people starved and piled up on the roadside... what do they care? ...They are there, and we are here... What'll we do? ...They'll have us on our knees... starve us... we'll be in no state to reason or defy. 'God save Ulster... We are the People... Up King Billy... United we stand... For God and Ulster... Remember 1690... and Derry's Walls... and now, can we have some milk and food please... please? We've to hold out while they twist England's arm. She'll have to act. She can't afford to ignore the will of the people. 'It'll be worth it... it'll be worth it,' they said.

As there was no electric, no television and no light, Peter suggested they make up their own entertainment. 'I'll be a reporter, I'll use my tape recorder, luckily I got a few batteries for it last week, so we don't have to worry about the electric.' He hurried down to his room.

'I'm going to pretend I'm a reporter, witnessing a riot outside this window,' Peter said as he pulled his chair forward. He propped the recorder carefully on the table.

He grinned, pressed the button, and held up the microphone. 'This is Dicky Duckins from the *Evening Standard* (you know, that English paper). I've been sent over to this primitive place to see what makes these people, I mean these savages, tick.' He coughed. 'Let me put you in the picture because, just by chance, I can see large crowds gathering outside my window, and between you and me I'm glad there is glass separating us, jolly glad indeed. I can see these natives, I mean these people, amassing on all sides... My word, they look a hostile lot.' He peered through the window with great concentration. He was encouraged by his mother's giggle and Sharon's condescending smile.

'I note they have equipped themselves for battle. There's arrows, tomahawks, pitchforks, and guns... and what's this I see? A rival gang coming from the opposite direction. This lot look really stone-age material, sloping foreheads, loincloths, and carrying clubs... Ah! There goes a club into the air, and another, and another... and there's a bottle, followed by a huge brick.. Now they are all tearing into each other. I hear a shot, and another one... They're murdering each other!' Peter's voice mounted with excitement. 'There's five down now, six, seven. I see ten men lying down in pools of blood. One man is standing on another's chest. He is drinking from a bottle. He has a gun in his hand. He is pointing it this way – at me! Whee!' Peter fell to the ground, then jumped up again. 'Sorry for the interruption, folks. I thought I had been shot. Someone had the audacity to try and stop me telling this to the world, but it's my grim duty to continue. My duty is plain.'

Margaret and her daughter Sharon giggled hysterically.

'Yes, my duty is plain. Good reporters have to risk their lives in the interest of news and truth. Golly, what's that... and that... a bit of leg, an arm, there's lumps of flesh sticking to that tree. I can hear the siren as the ambulance comes along. They are trying to stop it getting through. The men are bringing in the stretchers... they're shovelling them all up. They're putting bits into plastic bags now, and that fellow is removing limbs from that tree. My! He does look funny carrying that leg over his shoulder, and now they've done a good job indeed with their sweeping brush, a very good job indeed.' He coughed again and concluded. 'Well, folks, I think I've recorded all the excitement for an ordinary sunny Belfast afternoon, so I must return you to the studio. Good afternoon, everybody, good afternoon.'

'Little ghoul! What a mind!' Sharon declared. 'You've been watching too much television.'

Their mother stood up and walked towards the window. There wasn't a soul in sight. Not a light. It was a dead city. Dead silence. Something menacing lay just beneath the surface. She shivered and in an impulse drew the curtains.

'What are you doing? You'll be leaving us in the dark,' Peter protested.

'We'll close out the world, we'll light those candles and I'll bring in the supper.'

She set the three cups on the tray, put a small quantity of milk and suger in each, buttered a few scones, filled the kettle and put it on the stove. She struck a match. Nothing happened as she turned the knob.

'Bloody, bloody strike!' she hissed as she threw the match away in disgust.

Lost Roots

Anne Strain

She comes they say of Planters' stock
deeply entrenched in Ulster.
Usurper's stock
she turns away from the south.
Her kinsmen look to the rising sun
yet for her there's nothing there
but a wind of tears
a cold east wind and bitter.
Bewildered she finds her spirit rides
with the spirit of Cúchulain,
and her roots are as strong and deep
as the ancient Dóire.
And bewildered she asks
in her Planter's tongue
from where comes the blood
in the veins that leap
at the sound of an ancient language
she cannot speak.

The Girls in the Big Picture

Sandra Marshall

It was back in the early sixties
When me and my best chum, Pat,
Decided to try something different:
We were scunnered wi' this and wi' that.

Our big night out was a Saturday,
At the Orpheus you'd find us there,
But first to the Viking for a couple of drinks
And a quick check-up on the hair.

We rocked and we rolled and we twisted,
A right pair of ravers back then,
And if we didn't click we dandered on home
With a pastie supper from Ken's.

Then suddenly one day, just outta the blue
I turns round and says to Pat,
'Come on, you and me will join the Air Force.'
Says she til me, 'Why not?'

Our Mas and Das thought us mental
But they didn't object just the same,
so we threw a big going-away party –
I think half of Belfast came.

So off we sailed for England
Not knowing when we'd return.
As we waved goodbye to our families
We both had a good oul' gurn.

We arrived next day at lunch-hour,
Both of us knackered and done.
In no time we were out there marchin'.
Stickin' out! The Field, here we come.

Well, we couldn't do it for laughin' –

If you'd seen the cut of us –
Till the officer in charge let a gulder,
'Who's causing all that fuss?'

Up at half-past six every morning,
The middle of the night it seemed,
As we stood at our beds like zombies:
For inspection all had to be clean.

The grub we got was rotten,
One luk and we wanted to cry,
'For God's sake wud somebody bring us
A lovely big Ulster fry!'

At a lecture one day they asked us
Who joined just to get a man.
I nearly died, I was cut to the bone
When Pat stuck up her hand.

The officer looked at her odd-like,
She says, 'Is that rightly so?'
Pat just shrugged her shoulders,
'Aye, well, sort of a way, you know.'

Everybody called us Paddy.
That really got on our wick.
By Friday we'd just about had it,
We were starting to feel homesick.

We were sent to the commanding officer
To explain why we wanted out.
Thon oul' doll, I'll never forget her,
She made Hitler luk like a Boy Scout.

'You Irish girls have no backbone,'
She screamed at me and Pat.
'I'm from Belfast and I'd never go back.'
The two of us thought, 'Thank Jesus for that.'

We hadn't tuppence, no boat-fare home.

The Air Force lent us it.
We promised faithfully to pay it back –
They are waitin' on it yit.

We arrived back home on the Saturday,
Not even a full week away.
The sleggins we had to put up with
I've never forgot to this day.

We kept a low profile for ages,
The shame was too much to bear.
I can still hear the fellas shoutin',
'Is that the two rejects there?'

So it was back to the Orpheus on Saturday,
A bit more resigned to things.
To hell with leaving Belfast,
To hell with wantin' wings.

I'm sitting with Zen

Geraldine Reid

I'm sitting with Zen
Pondering the Art
Of music. The poetry of Strauss
I'm tuning my thoughts up…
I enjoy Thinking Quietly.
Outside the birds are singing
Evening is falling.
Life is mellow, my plant thriving.
I'm sitting with Zen
Relaxed… time has no claim on me.
It just passes by and I wave.
Freddy from the flat across the road
Cools beer on his window ledge
In expectation of a party
I expect – want! – nothing.
Strauss is waltzing
And I am the princess at the Ball.

The Comedian
Blanaid McKinney

Tragedy: when I cut my finger.
Comedy: when you fall down a manhole and break your
    neck.
Tragedy: the original.
Comedy: natural, logical extrapolations of that.
See children? See the funny pathologist reconstructing
all our faces from a single skull.

When young, we are stuffed with youngness, and the
    joins
don't show. A few naifs are shaken loose;
the rest are sluiced through grills of adulthood.
Leaving blood and nails and other bits of themselves
    behind.
Nobody seems to mind very much.
A life can be spent on secret returns, the reaching back
of pining, playpen fingers.

Here he comes
and stands in frozen eloquence on the edge of the stage.
Before any words, an internal tango. Other's-salt-
    picking
apes look up and say, 'This is not a young man
in a young man's body. This is a starved pixie on acid,'
then resume pelt-peering. Black soul in white jacket
opens his mouth, wide as his oracular eyes.

The Nazi had a sister – a real health food crank;
crocheted her own bread.
Couldn't get a ticket for the big event,
so she went to a hanging instead.

He can't afford any melt-in-the-mouth choreography.
His anger is skipping sideways; he grabs his art
by the scruff, word-furrowing. His Byzantine face
is spitting and planting rows of teeth under our seats.

123

Mine-fangs. Dangerous, ever-popping insomniacs.
Picture this. Then picture a stand-up there were these
      three.
Externalised lives and emptiness,
they own a million points of passing reference;
the gag. This ruptured panther is neither a stand-up
nor a lie-down, but a violent medium. Conjure up spirits
with knotted, arctic brisure, a needed exactness.
The violence of books re-opened, or a cleaned grave.
A young man's celebratory misery has made a peculiar,
poisonous kind of sense.
Altitude demands the ballast be dumped.

He's afraid and plumbs our minds, sounding out the
      snipers:
we are very cruel to our heroes.
Dutiful, a few floating sons and daughters
are still taking savage care of the civilised.
Picture this.
A roomful of competing comedians. One looks sad.
'What's the matter with him?'
'His mother just died.' 'His mother just died?
You think that's funny? Wait'll you hear this one…'

Tragedy: a small elastoplast.
Comedy: feed the animals. Making sure.
That we do not die.
Before we are killed.

Dora

Polly Devlin

(Chapter from a forthcoming novel)

'How was Belfast?' she said.

'I love Catholic women,' he said and then stopped.

'I'm not telling you anything, you just write it down,' he said. 'It's all right for you. I'm a director. I'm in the business of being a voyeur, of looking into other people's lives. But I don't expect it to happen to me. And what's more it's written from such a woman's point of view.'

'It would be, wouldn't it,' she said. 'I'm a woman.'

'When I read it first I didn't know what it was. Then I came on the phrase "balls in butter" and I knew who it was, and I laughed and then as I continued to read I got sadder and sadder. You saw things in such a different way. And all the time I was here you were thinking like that.'

He didn't say 'and watching'.

'You're so silly,' she said. 'You couldn't be more wrong – that isn't how writing is made. You're not just a recorder. What you read isn't just a simulacrum of what's happened. It just shows how good it is if you think that's what happened, as if Monet's garden was just like that. What you read was life compressed over days and days, different conversations and interpretations. Writing has to do with memory, sieving, filtering, pressing, perception and expressing. What you heard, experienced, observed, perceived, and rendering it down to tell some home truths: and *you* say it's voyeurism, some fast diary-entering. You've got a lot of nerve. You don't know your ass from your elbow.'

He bounced on the sofa and slugged his champagne.

'The reason I'm feeling a tiny bit – only the vaguest

bit –' he warned 'buoyant is because I think I've got a slot for two of the things I want to do next year, I *think* I have.'

'Oh great,' she began, and then modified her enthusiasm in case she reminded him that he had to be discreet. His struggles with his theatre company were already legendary. He looked sideways at her. What her mother had always called an old-fashioned look.

'I've discovered the secret of politics in that place,' he said, 'and how to get your way. You *never* leave the room for a pee. If you leave the room for a pee the programme you've planned in the schedule vanishes. I'm compromising too much, politicking with them, aren't I?'

She was surprised by the question. He was *young*. Young and good.

'No,' she said. 'I think that what you're doing is working within the system you've chosen to work in. That's how that system operates – and if you don't go along with it you won't get anywhere. That's not compromising – that's politics, work and career.'

He didn't ask whether she thought he was compromising by being there at all.

'What schedule? What plays?'

'In the autumn and before Christmas. The Beckett and the new Stevenson play.'

'And what about Stevenson wanting to direct?'

'I didn't bother to bring that up again. But I'll probably lose the scheduling anyway. I was watching the chaos of that place, the kind of deliberate havoc he creates, the way he treats even grown-up men...'

There was suddenly a break in the tempo of his talk, as though suddenly a second of time had slipped sideways into some small gap created by what he said, some link with something previous or prospective, like the stutter of a video sequence edited two or three frames out of kilter, and she knew it was the making of sense she had heard, the distance between him uttering the words and realising what he had said and he glanced suspiciously over at her to see if she had noticed and saw that she had her hand over her mouth and was laughing, rocking, seething with pleasure and delight too. Her testimonies through the post *had* had their effect.

'Even who, love?' she said. 'Tell me again.'

He was laughing too.

'Even grown-up men,' he said between gasps.

After a while, when they had composed themselves, she said, 'So what happened in Belfast?'

'Why didn't you come to Belfast?' he said.

She was silent. She was thinking of how unreachable even the idea of Belfast had been the week before and how close it was now. She said, hesitating, wondering what reasons she was going to produce, 'Partly prudence. I'm quite well known now. I know it's a long time since I acted there but they have long memories in Belfast.'

'Jesus, haven't they just,' he said.

'And partly too because you've been quite hostile lately.'

'Have I?' he said. 'Hostile.' He was silent for a while.

'Was it a great success?'

'Oh yeah. It was great. It was so strange to be back. You forget. Even the man driving the bus from the airport could only have been in Ulster. He's driven the route for sixteen years – he told me,' he added hastily. 'Christ, it's twenty questions every time we open our mouths.'

'I never uttered,' she said.

'No, but it was just there, I saw the question. And a man, a passenger off the plane, leaned in and asked him did he go such and such a place, was it on the route, and the man relapsed into this kind of speculative dream, wondering whether he did or not and everyone got drawn into this... this kind of verbal itinerary. Finally the passenger just went off, dazed. That never happens here. I mean the driver was genuinely curious as to whether he might go on that route today... he's been on the same route for sixteen years, but you never know.'

'The cruelty of circumstance,' she said. 'Thomas Hardy.'

'Then when I got to Belfast I went to my friend's house, Myles, he was in bed ill, he'd taken to his bed the day before, at the idea of me arriving. He was very poorly.'

'Cor,' she said, 'and was he ill the whole time?'

'Oh, he got better the minute I arrived. We got so drunk every night we seemed to stay up for ever – and there's so much happening. The last time I was there the streets were deserted, the shops barred, the pubs barricaded. Now there are night clubs and people everywhere, it's fantastic. And there were parties every night. We were the big-time theatre directors. Great.'

'When was the last time you were there?'

'When I left school. I left when I was eighteen. The first night I ever spent in Belfast was also my first day at boarding school.'

'You went to school there?'

'Yeah. You know that.'

'You lived in *Kent* and you went to school in Belfast? Your parents sent you to school in Belfast? But everyone was leaving.'

'I know, I know. He'd been there. To Campbell, he wanted me to have the same education.' He started to laugh again. 'Anyway, the first night I arrived I went up to the dormitory and all of us, all these strange new boys were handed a roll of Sellotape and told to Sellotape all the windows. I thought it was just another mad ritual in the whole mad world of boarding-school. During the night there were these enormous explosions. Thump, thump and everything was falling, shattering, you could hear the glass breaking everywhere. But not our glass – *our* glass was Sellotaped, wasn't it.'

'I see. So going back without the Sellotape must have been very nice.'

'It was great. On the last night there was a party up the Malone Road.' He put on a refined voice. 'Very smart.'

'I thought you liked Catholic women,' she said,

crossly. 'You wouldn't find many Catholic women up there.'

'Oh Christ, you're living in the Dark Ages. The Sellotape ages. This was at least half Catholic, half Protestant. I've never met such randy women as there were there. Jesus. Their husbands are in the next room and there's two women on either side of you in the kitchen saying how would you like to be licked all over, on one side by a Catholic tongue, on the other by a Prod.'

'And how would you?' she asked.

'Just thinking about it, just as they were talking gave me a hard-on.'

'And did they?'

'Practically. They took off my shirt. There I was, standing in this kitchen, half-naked and...'

'What would have happened if a husband had walked in?' she said, cross with herself for asking the question yet driven with curiosity.

'Exactly what I thought, but I was too far gone to care. One might have done for all I know. When I flew back I was in bed practically all next day, in the foetal position. I couldn't wake up and when I woke up I couldn't get up.'

'What happened when you went to visit O'Donovan?'

O'Donovan was a playwright who had great success on both sides of the Atlantic.

'He said, "Why are you working over there?" He put on an Ulster accent. "We need you here. What do you think you're doing *there*? We've no directors here. You must work here."'

'Would you like that?'

'It's an amazing place, the things that are happening, and the acting is terrible. Terrible.' He began to laugh again. Then he was serious, as serious as when he had asked if he was compromised by dealing with a system that dealt in deals. 'O'Donovan said I should come back. That I owed it to the country to come back.'

'That's not true. You owe the country nothing. A feeling of moral superiority on his part that may or may not be true. I'm certainly ambivalent enough about that old chestnut to wonder if it's not always used as emotional blackmail. It's what every artist who stays at home always says because they're frightened that in staying in their native country they have literally stayed *behind.* They're afraid that what they present as moral courage in their commitment to their nation, to *their* prospect of mind, is, at the bottom, moral cowardice and a fear of the foreign landscape – or mindscape I should say.'

He stared at her over the glass of champagne. This time he was laughing at her. She was off, launched into her didacts.

'And of course those who leave – like *me* – advance precisely these arguments in order to justify their desertion. Circus animals all, whether we go or stay. But all I can say is that those who have gone have paid back – in every sense of the phrase – their native land, far more, in full, that those who have stayed behind. Think of Joyce. Jesus: he didn't feel he owed his country anything. Silence, exile and cunning, though he was as cunning as a clucking hen and he never shut his bleedin' mouth.'

'Oi,' he said, desperately, but she hadn't finished, she was well launched, over her own inertia, into the strato.

'And not only did he feel he didn't owe Ireland anything, he felt *she* owed him, even to the extent of him resenting any change. He wanted her to stay exactly as she was, and she was in as bad trouble in 1904 as in 1984.' She drew breath. 'So, when is François getting back?'

'On Monday.'

'Are you looking forward to that?'

'It'll be nice to have things just being... normal, being back to normal.'

There was another silence. She drank champagne; she felt friable as though all the bits of her body were only just sticking together, like wet sand. Just another jolt from some angle she was shored up against and she would just slither apart, spread out, gravel and damp on the sofa.

'I want to go on seeing you,' he said in an utterly

conversational tone. 'But I don't think I should sleep with you.'

'Fine,' she said, equally conversational, the sand had coagulated, she was more firmly stuck together now, that kind of remark either tightened you up ('pulled yourself together' her mother would have said, along with another old-fashioned look), or blew you apart.

'It's been a strange day,' she said. 'Not the sort of one I'd like to have too often. First in the morning I'm told my mother has run off and left my father – after forty years. The bitch. She's always managed to evade and escape, but this is the best so far. Especially as she's never run anywhere in her life. Then I'm told my son has run away from school. He's been brought back. So I'm not great as a daughter and I'm lousy as a mother. Then I had another of those question-and-answer sessions about my film in which I'm torn apart, my blood's running down the screen. So there's been a lot of running. And then I'm told,' she looked away, staring hard at a bowl full of pot-pourri, concentrating fiercely on an external object as she had learned to do as a child when the pain in her throat had choked her but she would not cry. Now, as then, she could feel the tears rising up in her body, passing various levels until they reached their drain-pipes, her orifices where, if she didn't stare, frozen, they would spill out, eyes, ears, nose, through holes and spouts in her skin she didn't know she had.

'Go on.'

She said angrily, looking away, the tears just lipping at the edges, but she was holding them steady, 'I will go on. I need a moment to compose myself.'

It was he, of course, who made the movement that tipped the whole lot over, moving to put his arms around her, to stroke her hair, her face, to embrace her as though she was a child, to give her comfort in a way she had thought it impossible for men to give comfort, in this way that she had, a thousand times, given comfort and consolation to her stricken children, but which she had never before been given; and had not thought it possible

131

to receive. For she thought such comfort, such an imaginative encompassing of hurt, could only come from a woman and she could never take it from another woman, or had never asked for it, had never been able to ask for it from a woman, since she had not, she believed, first received it spontaneously from *the* woman when it was her only due. And if she had asked for it now, mutely, angrily, it was surely only because she knew, at some fundamental level, that no man could ever answer such a mute call, or even hear it, sense it rather, a call made only by the silent howl of pain squeezing its suffocated way through skin. The silent cries of the birth of pain. But he'd heard and here he was, the mother, the father, the man, the creature, with his arms around her imprecating, cursing, loving, stroking her, questioning, kissing.

'Who gave you a hard time at the session. You didn't go without anyone?'

She told him in detail of the angry audience, of the factions: the Protestants shouting that she had misrepresented them, the Catholics accusing, insisting she had betrayed them. 'Your own kind,' one had roared from the back. 'You're a Quisling.'

She had stood it out and answered the attacks as best she could, but no one in that audience of professional politicians had seen her film as anything other than a partisan documentary. She had become so accustomed to it being discussed as art, as a piece of personal vision, before it was analysed that she had forgotten that it might be seen from a wholly different viewpoint, a different set of ethics and aesthetics, or a lack of them. These people had looked at the film only to search for their own counterpart, to find their own viewpoint or the opposing one, they had viewed it like ferrets snuffling along corners and edges for burrows and the kill. They were bigots and philistines, *that* she knew: yet so foolhardy was she, and so conceited, she told herself, conceited, that she had thought to make them jump into the place she had portrayed in the film – an Ulster different from the ones they each insisted was the only true one.

'But you're mad to have gone there alone,' he said. 'You can't have expected them to see your film as it is? Any bunch of experts always gets it wrong. And those aren't experts at anything except bigotry and blame. It's like a bunch of lawyers reading *Crime and Punishment* – all they do is nit-pick about the faults in Dostoievsky's portrayal of the judicial system under the Tsars.'

She sniffed, burying her head on his shoulder like any Mills and Boon heroine.

'Why didn't you ask me?' he said. 'You had to have someone there who could show them what sort of film this way, make them see it not as something they could just scream about or try to rebut, or insult, but as *your* work, as a work of art, as a film that tells you about the whole thing and not just their awful eye-view of it. It's what made me fall in love with you, seeing that film: and you go along and show it and let them get away with all their prejudices intact, plus having done you in.'

'Come on,' he said, rising to his feet. 'We're going to bed.'

She knew it was no panacea but in the ceaseless quest it was something.

'We can't,' she said. 'You've decided not to.' She was pulling off her dress as she said it and peering out from its folds, watching his lovely body emerge from its strange inchoate garments. 'The last thing in that catalogue of failures I was reciting was going to be "and my lover told me he wasn't going to sleep with me any more, so I'm a failure as a lover". But then I didn't want to make an O'Donovan of myself.'

She pulled her dress over her head so that, even if she were being filmed, no one could have seen that she was grinning. Through the folds of material she heard him say: 'Catholic woman.'

133

Rabelais

(for Ian)

Blanaid McKinney

Lie down and stay,
And give to me
Your affectionate skin.

Give your creole face
To the watching woman,
Its familiarity tidy

And frightening.
Become recountable are
Love's colossal details;

The odd glimpse
Of a proud spine,
Such grudges, and grasps

At immediacy.
The cartoon certainty
Of previous obsession,

and animal scrum
Of hearts, motifs
Of leathery indifference.

But the sight of your
Sure and shouldering walk
Along the shouting stones

Of the Row, will earn
Always my serious
Applause in the night.

So stay and lend
Ambition to the watcher,
And we could have,

In love's mobile pedigree,
Something more severe
Than laughter.

The Secret Share
Christine Hammond

Bring me to it again, the secret share
in the heat and the paradisal half-light
there I lie with you,
and we are bid labour in love;
one to the other
with the other
for the other
while indistinct in the blue mirror
I view these letters for my alter ego
in focus,
dimming
words without voice:
'it is I'
dilating and closing on your sigh.

Limbo

Brenda Murphy

I sit clutching yesterdays like a vice in my mind, squeezing from them memories to wrap myself in. I sit disliking today and fearing tomorrow. I feel separate, apart, discarded.

I go to bed and wrap myself in an old, faded nightdress. I can exist in this state of limbo for days. But it passes, always to come back unasked.

This human skin I'm in contains all those emotions, good and bad. It can still surprise me with sudden outbursts of love and lust. Lust for the same person I've loved for years. It is so unexpected. Weeks of indifference can be turned into a tangled, laughing, serious, soft-worded loving. And the glow can last for days. The rumpled bed lies unmade until late the next day to try and preserve a while the joy I've had there.

I'm stupid like that. Hard to take I am, my love. I shut you out so much. My tongue is razor-sharp and I can cut you with it and do. I try to watch it, watch my words, guard you from an anger I cannot explain, which you do not cause. But it goes full circle and comes back to limbo again.

Woman Alone

Ruth Hooley

This is the person she is –
Leaning out of doors against the wall,
Holding the sun to her after rain.

Eyes chasing a small lithe figure,
Blur of a childhood breeze
Rippling through long grass.

Cast in her own role,
Barely attached – only by a string
To the lingering shadow

That creeps across dimly-lit rooms,
Staring discreetly at dusk
From a thinly veiled window and

Falling across his bed to vanish there
In disembodied dark:
This is the person she is,

Leaning out of doors against the wall,
Sun after rain, seeding her own grain –
Lifting the mist over Eden.

All I Ask

Maura Johnston

All I ask is to find myself.
Face gone in the mouth of the mirror
My voice soars soundless.
My hands rifled your treasures,
Feet echoed yours. Slack on the shelf
Of my stomach you rested.
Rain pats the roof with remembering fingers.

Letting Go

Anne Jago

Seeing you again
After all this time,
Wanting to laugh, to cry
To touch, to hold
Is buried in a handshake.

Oh, to burst through
The stained glass window
Of your civilised conversation,
Only to to crumble
Wasted cooling embers.

Losing you haunts me
Like a whispered threat.

The Reprisal

Jill McKenna

'Hey! Hey boy! What d'you think you're doin'? Tom,
get the hold of him, quick!'

Joe Best made a grab for the boy as he dived out of
the barn in the wake of his fleeing companion. The boy
wrenched himself free, but Tom, with a flying tackle,
brought him down before he had run more than a few
steps.

'Tom, get after yon other one.' The farmer pointed
after the first youth, who was already halfway across the
nearest field. He dropped his arm. 'Ach, never bother.
We'll get his name from this lad here – if we don't, the
police'll get him soon enough.'

He looked down at the second youth, who lay
where he had fallen, staring up at the big weatherbeaten
farmer and his strapping son. His expression was de-
fiant, but there was fear there as well. Joe reckoned he
was about sixteen years old at the most. He was thin, and
wore old jeans and a yellow teeshirt.

Bending down, he gripped the boy's arm and
hauled him roughly to his feet. 'What were you doin' in
there?' he rasped.

''Snone of your business.' The boy's thin body quivered slightly.

'It's my business when you do it in my barn,' Joe
said grimly. He turned to his son. 'Away in there and
find out what they were doin'. I'll hold on to this young
lad here.'

Tom went into the barn and came out again hastily.
'There's a thing on the floor,' he reported. 'Like a box,
with somethin' stickin' out of it. It looks like a bomb.
Let's get out of here, quick!'

'What about my barn?' Joe Best shook the boy
angrily. 'Is that thing goin' to go off?'

The boy glared at him in silence. Joe hit him hard on

the side of the head. Tears started in the boy's eyes and his lower lip quivered, but he said nothing. Joe felt a twinge of remorse.

'Let's get out of here, Daddy,' Tom pleaded. 'The wee bugger's not goin' to say anything'. We could get killed just standin' here.'

'All right,' said Joe reluctantly. 'Give us a hand.'

Father and son gripped an arm each and the boy was frogmarched briskly through the farm gate, past the outbuildings and through the back door of the house and the scullery into the old-style kitchen, with its open fire and scrubbed stone floor. There was no one there.

'It's lucky your ma's away into town,' Joe said, looking round.

'D'ye think we're far enough away?' Tom asked anxiously.

'Maybe not. Better take him into the parlour.'

They took the boy through the narrow hallway into the front room – gloomy and austere, with a leather horsehair sofa, two straight-backed chairs and a heavy Victorian table with a vase of dried flowers placed mathematically in the centre. The fireplace was concealed by a glass-covered screen, with 'Simply to thy Cross I Cling' embroidered painstakingly on it by some long-dead hand. Yellowing photographs of stony-faced couples stood stiffly on the upright piano; and a framed copy of the Ulster Covenant took pride of place above the mantelpiece. The afternoon was warm, but only a narrow strip of sunlight penetrated the chilly room. The boy shivered.

His captors pushed him down on the sofa and stood over him. Joe wondered where to start. He wasn't used to interrogating teenage bombers.

'Right now,' he said at last, sternly. 'What's your name then?'

''Snone of your business,' the boy replied stubbornly.

'Will I beat it out of him, Daddy?' Tom asked, too eagerly.

Joe looked with barely concealed distaste at the

140

fleshy, pink-cheeked face. He hated to admit it, even to himself, but sometimes he disliked his only son with an intensity which frightened him. There was a sadistic streak in him which he found hard to stomach.

'No,' he said. 'No, we'll get it out of him without that.'

He turned to the boy. 'Why'd you do it, son? Why pick on me?'

The boy stared silently at his feet. Joe tried again. 'Did they tell you to do it?'

'Who?'

'Them. The I.R.A. or yon other crowd.'

'No.'

'You're lyin'.'

'I'm not. Honest to God they didn't.'

'You mean it was a do-it-yourself job?'

'Aye.'

'Well, why? I mean, I'm not in the U.D.R. or anything. Neither's Tom.'

The boy glanced round the room like a trapped animal seeking a means of escape. There was none. His eyes flickered over the Ulster Covenant and then back to his feet. He sighed. 'All right,' he said. 'It was a reprisal.'

Joe was bewildered. 'A reprisal? A reprisal for what?'

'I can't tell you.'

'You'd better tell us, you rotten wee bastard,' Tom interjected, breathing heavily. 'You and your Fenian friends – you're the scum of the earth, so you are.'

'Lay off, Tom,' Joe said angrily. 'You know I don't like that sort of talk.'

He turned back to the boy. 'You may as well tell us – because you're goin' to have to tell the police anyway.'

The boy said nothing, but his body tensed at the mention of the police. He glanced up at Joe, then away again. The older man had a strong feeling of recognition.

He turned to Tom, who was watching the boy like a cat eyeing its prey. 'Away and ring Sergeant Nixon at the barracks and tell him we got a bomber. And when you've done that make us a cup of tea. I'm parched.'

141

Tom looked sulky. 'Why don't you phone him? I'll watch this fella here...'

'No, you won't. Go on – out!'

Tom left, slamming the door behind him. Joe and the boy looked at one another in silence. The silence deepened and lengthened. The boy looked away, studying his fingernails with careful concentration.

Joe opened his mouth, shut it again and sat down on the sofa beside the boy. 'You remind me of someone, son,' he said, slowly and deliberately. 'Someone I haven't set eyes on for a long time. Kathleen Donnelly. Kathleen McBride she is now.'

The boy glanced up, startled, colour flooding into his cheeks. For an instant his eyes met Joe's – then he looked back at his fingernails.

'That so?' he muttered.

'You must be her son. Hers and Francie's. Is your name McBride?'

'No... no it isn't. I never heard tell of them.'

'You're lyin', son – and you're a bad liar. You might as well admit it – sure it'll all come out anyway when the sergeant gets the hold of you.'

The boy suddenly sprang to his feet, poised for flight. Quick as a flash Joe reached out and grabbed his arm.

'Don't try it, son,' he said softly. 'I'm not that stupid. Sit down and have a wee bit of sense.'

The boy sat down reluctantly, his eyes bleak. 'All right,' he said. 'All right, you win. But it's got nothin' to do with me da. He doesn't know I'm here. When he finds out he'll kill me. He thinks you're a good man.'

'And you don't?'

'No.'

'Why not?'

'You stopped him gettin' a council job. A vet's assistant.'

'What d'ye mean I stopped him?' Joe asked, bewildered.

'You and the other Unionists on the council. You voted for Bertie Mathers instead. My da was better qualified – sure you know he's good with animals. He used to treat your cows when they took sick. Bertie'd hardly know one end of a cow from the other – but he's a Protestant. You're supposed to be my da's friend, but you voted against him.'

'No I didn't.'

'Yes you did.'

'I didn't... at least, if I did, I didn't mean to. A lot of these things are decided behind closed doors. In committee.'

'Sure you'd have voted against me da anyway, even if you'd have known. The D.U.P. says jump and you jump. That's what me da says anyway.'

Joe was silent. The boy pressed on. 'You want to see the place we're livin' in. You wouldn't put a dog in it. It's got black stuff growin' up the walls and no bathroom or anythin'. Your animals are better housed than us.'

'That's not our fault. That's the Housin' Executive.'

'Aye, but you and your mates voted against the housin' estate they were goin' to build at Kilbeg.'

'That's because we reckoned it was a waste of public money.'

'Oh aye. A waste of money – to rehouse the likes of us?'

He turned his head and glared at Joe with Kathleen's grey eyes. The sight of them in the pale, boyish face made his throat contract painfully, even after twenty-odd years.

All those years ago his father had put his foot down. No son of his was going to marry a Papist. If he did, he would be disinherited. He would lose the farm and land, and he wouldn't get a penny. To listen to him, you'd have thought she was a witch.

His eyes moved from the Covenant, signed in blood, to the framed photograph of his father on the piano. He knew every feature of it by heart. It was a hard, unyielding face with a hint of cruelty about the thin mouth. Tom sometimes reminded him of his father, though he didn't look like him.

His father had been buried many years now, but he

still had a lot to answer for, Joe thought grimly. He had married Margaret. A nice enough woman, but his father's choice, not his. And she had given him Tom...

'I could've been your father,' he said, half to the boy and half to himself. After he'd said it, he wished he hadn't; but the boy nodded.

'I know. Me mother told me.'

He could have been – but he wasn't.

He became aware that he was staring at the boy. With an effort, he brought himself back to the task in hand.

'Who was the other young lad?' he asked. 'The one with you.'

The boy looked at him warily. 'I'm not tellin' you – and I'm not tellin' the cops either. They can beat me to death, but I'm not sayin'.'

Joe sighed. 'Don't worry – I'm not goin' to make a martyr out of you.'

He broke off and they listened as a car purred its way up the lane to the farm.

'That'll be Sergeant Nixon now,' Joe said.

The boy said nothing. His teeth were clenched tightly on his lower lip. As Joe watched, his eyes slowly filled with tears.

Joe swallowed. He'd always been a law and order man – but this was different. He was Kathleen's son. How could he denounce him in court with her looking on?

He cleared his throat and came to a decision. 'Listen, son,' he said. 'I don't want to get you into trouble. You're too young to go to jail and have your life ruined. And I'm... I'm sorry about your ma and da. I'll see if I can get somethin' done for them – but it isn't easy.

'Now – Tom'll be lettin' the sergeant in the back door. Away you out the front, quick – and I'll tell him you kicked me and gave me the slip.'

The boy's face lit up and he jumped to his feet. 'My da was right, Mister Best,' he said. 'You're not too bad – for a Unionist.' At the door he paused, and a smile flickered across his face. 'Sorry about your barn.'

144

He was gone. Joe heard the front door closing softly at the same moment as a car door slammed in the yard.

Seconds later, the peaceful calm of the summer afternoon was shattered by a loud explosion.

Chivalry

Anne Strain

You told me
how with great decorum
you shook hands with her,
after Church,
saying how nice it was
to see her once again.

She, suitably demure,
an attitude expected
in those days
(especially on a Sunday)
thanked you, most sincerely,
for your welcome.

Both of you were secretly delighting
in the knowledge
that in your pocket lay
a pair of soft silk briefs,
memento of a previous evening's
tenderness.

After months of knowing one another,
exploring cities,
laughing in remote hills,
sharing words,
what possessed you, man,
to walk away
'for her own good'?
Surely it was a lover that she needed
not a hero.

He Haunts Me

Sheila Mulvenna

He haunts me like a dead person
He spoke of death so often.
He is with me so much, yet never.
I look for him everywhere
I only find resemblances, pieces of him in other men.
Ordinary men, ready to give what he could not
Willing to take what he could not
I shun them with his coldness.
Sleeping, he haunts my dreams,
Cruel, heartless, terrifying me with nightmares.
I awake frightened, sweating, shivering.
I look for reassurance, he is not there.
He would not give it if he were.

An Irish Fairy Tale

Frances Molloy

Once upon a time, in the land of saints and scholars,
there lived a handsome young man named Kevin. One
day he decided to retreat from the world and spend the
rest of his life giving praise to god as a holy hermit. He
then went to live high upon a ledge in a wild remote place
indeed, called Glendalough, in the county of Wicklow.
Now, there was also, at the same time, in the land of
saints and scholars, a beautiful maiden, whose name is
forgotten on account of the fact that it was never considered worth remembering. Well, didn't this beautiful
maiden fall madly in love with the holy hermit. She made
lots of attempts to talk to him, to get him to come down
off his lonely ledge, for she wanted him to fall in love
with her too and come away down and marry her. He
didn't want to at all so he did a lot of praying, meditating,
and confabbing with god, and after he was finished he
decided to put an end to her wooing – and he did. The
next time she came up to him he shoved her down off the
top of his high ledge and she got broke into smithereens
on the rocks far down below, and god was very pleased
with the holy hermit. When he died, many years later, as
an old, old man, the people of Ireland acclaimed him as a
saint. And ever since, droves of nuns, from all over
Ireland, converge on his tomb, annually, every year, to
pray for the great virtue of chastity as practised by holy
Saint Kevin, the patron saint of woman beaters.

When It Comes

Kate Madden

When it comes 5 o'clock
Or anywhere near
My body goes numb
I tremble with fear,
If he comes home at five
All may go well
Anytime later I know there'll be hell.
Sometimes I pray he won't come home,
Maybe tonight he'll leave me alone.
It's now 12 o'clock
And he's banging at the door,
Oh god he's drunk
I can't take it anymore!
I feel the first punch
And he's wrecking the place
I crawl to the corner
And cover my face.
If I move from this corner
I know I'll be dead
I feel one more kick to the side of my head –
He's kicked me so hard I cannot see –
There isn't an ounce of fight left in me.

I wake in the morning
Bruised and in pain
But at least it's all over
'Til it happens again.

The Charm School
Medbh McGuckian

No, she is not there, for all our elaborate
Eavesdropping. She is sewn into clothes
No woman could wear, she drags her coat
Along the cat-walk as if she had just killed it.

Dresses sing on her, the make-up
Will not stay upon her bridesmaid's eyes,
Her fully-fashioned lips, gracing
Matchboxes and carrier bags.

She pretends it is a story, her unhappy marriage
To that inveterate door-opener, that night
Is the best time to be intimate,
Its get-out clause no more than her due.

Morocco 1956*

Christine Hammond

The last valise
for better or worse
transient in the jeep.

Dog-day and swelter
silencing all
but the slamming of shutters

room after room and
voices resounding
upwards off cool, shaded tiles.

Two mosquitos stir
in a circle
above the bleached counterpane

she glances aside
bed to dresser:
a small silver frame –

the one item
idle and alone
she dared not pack:

Paris. 1950.
Before Independence.
Before the English woman:

Soon, they'd be in Paris again.
He'd beg her to change her mind.
There,
she'd tell him about leaving the photograph.

* In 1956 Morocco gained independence.

151

Solicitor's Office

Patricia Mallon

The shabby carpet sadly stares at threadbare marriages
That split and permit themselves to be funeralled off
In the unemotional cover of legal terms.

Sins of omission, sins of neglect,
Disharmony of living in a state of things undone;
Two split into one and one with the signing of names on
        the dotted line,

Alimony paying the piper for a tune already sung.

The Eighth Station
Francine Cunningham

The train moves.

The old man
offers his seat
to the smart
young woman.

Still Life

Eileen Kelly

Smiling the old man sits on a crude
wooden bench.
Furrowed brow, piercing eyes, grey
beard, clay pipe in hand.
Brown cord breeches, waistcoat, and
battered felt hat.
Shotgun in the right hand, wild
duck beside him dead.
Time does not age him, he is
immortal.
A flick of the duster, carefully
I set him on the shelf.

The Cage

Frances McEnaney

In an aroma of unaccustomed hair-oil and wearing his
badly wrinkled best suit, John Fitzpatrick sat in the front
seat of the church and wished he might be anywhere else
on earth. Middle-aged, balding and shrewd, he was in a
state of acute depression. The condition of his suit surprised him, for although he wore it every Sunday, he
hadn't noticed it was so grubby. As well as stains, it must
have stretched for it was big on him; this was odd – the
tailor had made a good job of it when it was new a year
ago. When he saw him again, he would tell him about it.
If he saw him again – for what did it matter now?

Determined to keep his panic-stricken thoughts at
bay, he looked for further distraction and found it in two
sets of initials in the arm-rest in front of him. They were
deeply carved and inlaid with the grime of years, but it
was a waste of time to try to put names to them. The
countryside was littered with J.D.'s and M.O'B.'s so he
allowed his eyes to travel over the counter-mapped grain
in the pitch pine. Here he was baulked once more for the
flow of line was punctuated by woodworm holes. He
glanced quickly up and down his seat and saw that it,
too, was riddled with them and the thought of so much
secret tunnelling going on right under him made him
lean forward on his haunches to prevent too much strain
on the weakened wood. Wouldn't it make you sick, he
thought, allowing the damage to go on unchecked and
who was to know how many adult beetles flew out of the
holes and took a free ride home with the congregation to
infest their innocent farm-houses? He shifted further
forward and the movement caused a fresh wave of hair-
oil to envelop him, resurrecting all the thoughts he desperately wanted to forget.

At the same instant he heard the bird and listened
intently. It patrolled the church in long, quiet sweeps,
anxious already, but not yet seeking freedom violently.

It fed, he supposed, on flies and spiders, and it would never go short of woodworm, but where would it get water? All animals had to be watered and yet you never heard of a dead bird in a church. Oh, yes, it would find freedom soon enough, while he was giving up his, to enter the dreaded cage of Matrimony.

Like a rat in a treadmill, his thoughts repeated the familiar litany that led to his present predicament. They always began with Sarah, his sister. She was ten years older than John and she mothered and spoiled him. Because of him she had missed her market and he knew it. But he had his independence and he gloried in it. To be fair to him, though, he had a well-deserved reputation as a hard worker and he extracted every ounce of value from the small farm. This freedom from domestic responsibility, however, was never more evident than on Sunday mornings after Mass when he joined a few of his bachelor cronies outside the church gate. It only needed the sight of a recently-married man going homewards with his wife to start him off.

'Will you look at him,' he always said. 'Look at him, caged and he doesn't know it. Another good man fallen into the trap.' And knowing John's feelings on the subject of matrimony, one of the men would always say, 'Now, John, it happens to the best of us.' He never failed to rise to the bait; indeed, he welcomed it.

'Begod, I'm one that'll never be caught and tamed!'

'The girl's not born yet, John, who'll catch you!' My God, he thought, as the sweat broke on him now, if only he hadn't said those words so often! But they were stamped on his mind as indelibly as they must be on his friends'.

He remembered walking into the kitchen that evening after a hard day in the far field. He was pleasantly hungry and the savoury smell told him Sarah's good meat pie was ready. Perhaps he might have been warned by the forbidden hen stepping and pausing across the spotless floor, but he scarcely noticed it, for beside a smashed mixing basin, and against the pantry door, Sarah lay dead.

On the morning after the funeral he overheard speculation about his future from the neighbours who had come in to help him.

'I hear there's no relatives to keep house for him,' a woman said. 'Of course I'll do what I can, but it won't be easy for I've my own family to look after. As it is, I'm all behind with my work. Can you think of anyone at all who'd come and do a hand's turn for him? I've thought but I can't come up with a soul. What do you think?' Her friend pursed her lips and shook her head meditatively.

'I doubt there's nothing left for him but a wife.'

'A wife! You must be joking, sure everyone knows the way he feels about marriage.'

'Mark my words, it'll come to that in the end, you'll see.' John was infuriated. So that was the way they were thinking, was it? Never! Never! He needed no wife nor ever would! He looked round the room. Sarah's clock continued marking seconds, the place was tidy. By heavens, he'd show them, he'd look after himself. A few potatoes, a bit of bacon, a pot of tea, there was nothing to it. The sooner he got rid of these women, the better he'd like it. It was high time for them to be off home anyway.

He joined the women, refused the inevitable cup of tea and thanked them all for their kindness. Then, in a chilly voice, he added that he did not wish to be beholden to them any longer and he could well look after himself. The touch of frost and carelessly chosen words silenced the women. One of them moved the ornaments on the mantlepiece unthinkingly, the other gathered up her things and prepared to leave. In a huffed voice she told John that she might look in on the following day to see how he was faring, but she had the distinct impression that a door had been slammed in her face.

For a while after Sarah's death the house seemed obedient to her clean touch but gradually neglect began to tell. Dirt from the yard caked the kitchen floor and bluebottles began a lengthy reign in the cool pantry. John discovered he was no cook. Sarah's method of making porridge seemed simple until he tried to copy it.

Potatoes either boiled into mush or were half-cooked and the endless cleaning of burnt saucepans was one more chore that sickened him. Sarah scorned bought bread but now the baker was a regular caller and nothing John bought from him compared with his sister's baking. Sometimes he would find himself staring at his dirty shirts lying in a bucket of water and willing them to emerge clean and well-ironed. But it was the loneliness of the evenings that affected him most. He missed Sarah greatly and when he could stand it no longer, he would wander off to an unmade bed.

The day the soot fell decided John's future. The kitchen chimney was overdue for cleaning and one morning, gorged by the huge fires that he made for comfort, it vomited its contents onto the floor with a dull clump. The mess was unbelievable. He did the best he could to clean the room, but now it seemed that everything he ate tasted of soot and everything he touched was covered with it. It was the last straw. He would have to marry.

He fought the idea for a few weeks, mainly because of the embarrassment he would feel when his friends knew of his decision, but he had no option. He needed a clean house, well-cooked food and a companion at night. But first he would have to see the doctor, his stomach was giving trouble and all the baking soda he took was not curing it.

The doctor guessed almost to the week when John would appear in the surgery. He was an old man, shrewd and kind, and having known John for many years he had made his diagnosis almost before John sat in the chair.

'So the baking soda's not doing the trick then, John?' he said, and taking in the man's whole run-down appearance, he leaned across the desk and said in an earnest voice:

'Now, John, scraps of food cooked any old way won't do, won't do at all. Let's face it, you're no cook and you never will be, so what's to be done? I can give you a bottle that will relieve some of the trouble but I can't cure you. I know what will though. What you need,

157

John, is a wife and the sooner you get one and settle down to regular meals and a clean house, the sooner your stomach will give you peace.' John said nothing. He looked, thought the doctor, like a man whose spirit had been broken. A plan began to simmer in the doctor's mind. 'Come back in a week's time, John, and I may have news for you.' John nodded dumbly.

The best farm at the other end of the practice belonged to old Mr Anderson. He was cared for by Mary Ellen, his timid, middle-aged, unprepossessing daughter. He had his own troubles. A few months earlier, the doctor had warned him to put his affairs in order but this seemed impossible, for there was no one to run the farm. When his daughter was younger he had received a few offers for her hand, but since all the suitors had less land than he, Mary Ellen remained single. Now, the question of her future and that of the farm ate like a rat into his sleepless nights. He bitterly regretted he had not found a husband for her, a smaller farmer would be a saviour now, if he was a good man and a hard worker. But the men who had wanted both his land and Mary Ellen were long since married and now his time was running out.

On the doctor's next visit to the old man, John Fitzpatrick's name was mentioned. The old man had heard of him and listened while John's case was presented. The 'match' was pathetically easy to arrange. Mary Ellen was informed of it, later.

John listened meekly while the doctor pointed out the various advantages of the match and he was struck by the bargain he was getting, in spite of the nagging at the back of his mind. Good food, a clean house and a large farm whose owner hadn't long to live. The thought of a wife still continued to make him wince.

To avoid the early wagging of tongues, the doctor, delighted that his plan was coming to fruition, drove John to the Andersons', late one night. Neighbours who heard his car did not comment, for he made frequent visits to the old man. John was not taken by Mary Ellen's appearance. From this time on he avoided his friends.

If Sarah was a good cook, Mary Ellen was a better one. Instinctively guessing at his home conditions, she went to great trouble for John's first meal with them, putting a power of energy and enthusiasm into the baking. He had left behind him a winter of white baker's bread, milk, pale tinned soups broken occasionally by the artificial pink of vague tinned meats. As he entered the dining room his eyes were ravished by exciting colours and his nose assailed by a small army of forgotten aromas, all of them delectable. There was a suspicion of spice, a hint of onion and a whisper of cooking apples. In his swift inventory of the table as he took his seat he counted four kinds of bread, three large cakes, a ham whose pink shimmered before his meat-starved eyes, salad that was a meal in itself and a crisp white meringue floating over what he hoped was a lemon meringue pie. John stared at Mary Ellen, admiration for her skill plainly evident in his look and she, daring to raise her eyes at that moment, caught the look and was satisfied.

They met twice a week, always at her home. When the old man was not with them they sat in separate pools of silence – resembling a married couple in whom the fount of words has long since died. Even in his presence, conversation between the two of them was difficult – often impossible.

But the room was never completely quiet for John was afflicted with a noisy digestion. Strangers to this insistent rumbling were often shocked into unbreakable silences. Like a band tuning up, it began quietly enough, increasing however in sound and variety, and filling the room with a sense of uneasiness. One day, when tea was long over and John was buried in a newspaper, the gurglings began. By this time Mary Ellen was somewhat used to them but not to the new note. Sliding up the scale, it finished in a high-pitched squeak. Something about the sound caught John's ear. He shook out his paper noisily and at the same moment, he caught Mary Ellen's eye. She was transfixed. 'Down Fido!' he commanded, slapping his side and grinning. Mary Ellen, freed at last from suppressed embarrassment, burst into a hearty laugh. Begod, he thought, the woman isn't half bad-looking when she laughs.

If there was little to learn from John by way of conversation and Mary Ellen's shyness did not help, she learned much by observation. One of her first jobs, she could see, would be that of mender, for he lacked buttons, his cuffs were frayed and his socks in holes. One day she timidly asked him to bring some of his clothes for mending, and when the parcel was opened she was dismayed to find that kangaroo halts of fleas had speckled the contents.

She had mixed feelings about the wedding. It was better not to think about it, she told herself, for she knew the man only through his clothes and his stomach. There was no doubt that his love of her cooking was his Achilles heel. If she had to work hard with this small bud of interest she would go to any lengths to achieve flowering. If he liked her cooking, he might come to like her. Love! She lit lightly on the word and just as swiftly flew away from it. She could never expect this from a stranger. A nervous rash broke out on her face when she thought of her wedding night.

It was to be a very quiet wedding due to Mr Anderson's infirmity, the maturity of the bride and groom and John's extreme fear of any publicity. The clear yellow of some last late dahlias glowed against the cream stone of the altar and high up, on one point of it, the bird had come to rest. The few guests relaxed for they had become extremely nervous during the bird's incessant flights. But there was no peace for John. Outside the church he could hear a small commotion and he began to sweat with panic. You could do nothing in this village, he thought, without everyone knowing about it. And he had purposely chosen the early hour when no one would be astir. But this was a petty irritation compared with the thought that some of his friends were already waiting out there for him. His best man looked at him uneasily. What, in the name of heaven, was the matter with the man, he'd done nothing but shuffle in his seat since they arrived?

160

A light rain had begun to fall when Mary Ellen arrived at the church. She nodded at the faces she recognised among the group gathered there and guessed there would be comments about her suit. She had been unhappy about it from the start. A saleswoman, anxious to unload a buyer's mistake, had steam-rollered her into a strident blue suit that highlighted her sallow complexion and accentuated her angular figure. The saleswoman had been cruel. Mary Ellen stood out like a beacon on a dull day. But her thoughts were already in the church. He doesn't like me, she thought, but God grant that we'll be happy together.

John's fears increased considerably when he heard the mild chatter grow to a swell as the church door opened. There was no time left now to avoid the cage, even the discomfort of the house he had left dimmed in retrospect.

When Mary Ellen joined him at the alter she looked at him shyly, and a small smile that began in her eyes froze before it reached her lips when she saw the expression on John's face.

Later, when they left the sacristy after signing the register, Mary Ellen, greatly daring, placed her hand inside John's arm, a gesture she might never make again. It made her self conscious and increased John's nervousness. But the pressure of her hand reminded him that his first duty as her husband was to walk with her down the aisle and into the waiting taxi. Around him was the murmur of the guests as they prepared to leave their seats. Outside the door lay the cumulation of all his fears.

The bird had gone, probably through the same door.

'Caught and caged. I'm one that'll never be caught in that trap!' There was a faint hope that if none of his friends was outside, he could slip into the taxi and the dreaded hurdle would be avoided.

When they reached the church door, the voices of the watchers burst into good wishes, but John scarcely heard them. Dear God, thought Mary Ellen, maybe it

161

won't be too bad. She looked at John but he missed her glance for he had already seen the group of men by the wall, and by their knowing looks he guessed at their conversation. Fresh sweat broke on him and his panic mounted higher. He imagined he could hear their jibes. He whispered to Mary Ellen but the words were lost in the rising voices of the crowd. Releasing his arm from hers, he walked carelessly across the gravel towards his friends and with a great show of bravado began to search for his pipe.

Mary Ellen felt a rising flush of embarrassment in the silence that fell among the guests and onlookers. The men by the gate stared at him, the shame of his action reflected in their faces. But he would show the world that he was still his own master.

'Ah say, boys,' he remarked encouragingly as he joined them, 'that's not a bad day for a wedding.'

In the back of the taxi when it finally left the church, the tears that Mary Ellen had choked back while she stood on the gravel now spilled down her crumpled face, dropping lightly on the dreadful suit. John stared unseeingly out of the window. What had possessed him? Wouldn't it have been better to have faced the music when the match had first been made and taken the ribbing like a man? Now, the whole countryside would soon know and it would never be forgotten, never. It was just the kind of cataclysmic action that would be handed down from one generation to the next.

'Did you hear of the time John Fitzpatrick left his bride at the church door and went over to talk to his friends at the gate?' My God, but it would make a great story, he could just hear the laughs.

It was some time before the sounds Mary Ellen was making registered with John and when they did he was aghast to discover she was sobbing, convulsive sobs that refused to be hidden. He had never heard the like since he was a child and his instinctive reaction was to assure himself that the partition between the driver and the back of the taxi was closed. That fellow was keeping a watchful eye on them anyway. Why didn't he attend to the road and get on with the driving, the nosey bastard? The heavy body-shaking sobs continued.

John forced himself to look at Mary Ellen's predicament and a grain of pity overlaid his frantic thoughts. Should he say something? He rehearsed a confession.

'I'm sorry, Mary Ellen, I'm sorry, I don't know what made me do it. I'm one ignorant bastard and I'd give anything in the world not to have done it.' But the words refused to come out. He practised again.

'Mary Ellen,' he would say, 'I'm sorry.' Four words. He opened his mouth and tried to force out 'Sorry,' but he couldn't say it. Anyway, it wouldn't get through to Mary Ellen, the way she was creating now. He'd have to shout and then the driver might hear the apology and add it to the scene his sharp eye was trying to piece together.

By now Mary Ellen had reined in her grief and only the little double sniffs of dying sobs reminded John of the original paroxysm. He pushed himself further into the corner so that he might observe her. She was staring straight ahead, immured in her own prison. Only her hands continued to twist and clench. In the name of God, why didn't she say something, anything to break the silence. She was waiting for him, he decided, to make the first move and he couldn't. Hadn't he tried? But the apology wouldn't come, not in the back of the taxi anyway.

Already John felt trapped. He was imprisoned behind the bars of matrimony, within the blank walls of a silence more deadly than any he had known in her father's house.

A picture flashed through his mind of the two of them in the long evenings of the winter days ahead and a finger of sadness lightly touched him and spread through his body filling him with despair. Would he ever be able to say he was sorry? Was the marriage to be locked for the rest of their days in this cage of silence?

One Autumn

Maura Johnston

A frog came into the kitchen
Right in the middle of the fourth

Decade, the one I gave out.
It sat where the Tilley poured

Its humming yellow circle. We
Wouldn't touch it in case of warts

And anyway the prayers continued
In drones and cushion muffled snorts

Of laughter, to the last of the trimmings.
Then we tried to catch it

On a shoe box lid, to tip it
Back awkward into the sated

Settled Autumn night.
Hectored, its blotched horny

Hide could barely bind its
Tiny pulse of life. Cornered

It sprang, with a sudden
Retching rise, right into

A basin of apple jelly. All
Day it had dripped, thin

Amber drops, essence of stubble
Fields and tightening dusk.

Crab apples. Gnarled old trees.
Arthritic contours masking

Plenty, like a barren bitch
Suckling twins. The flour bag

Swung, slung between table
And window, its sour

Squeezings ransoming her
Hours of hobbled hooking. Next

Day she gave it to the pigs,
Reluctantly, sad to let

Go her share in one
More Autumn; a shelf

Of pinioned praise, nostalgic
Proof of her solitary self.

Meleagris Gallopavo

Ann W. Gleave

Gobbler:
hunted and transported
from a land
of volcanic dust and gold;
nervous and wary,
proud in display,
now circles
in a compound
open neatly to the sky.
Hunted and transported
out of earshot
to isolation siege;
wild eyes
see no stars
no territory to claim
no sparkling water
of homeland
no nesting hen
to cover the eggs
with leaves.

Gobbler
runs for cover
skids round and round
in a wooden pen,
falls hard on the fence
submits
to food from an iron trough.

One last day
he is brought,
innocent
to the silent knife
to the cold stone floor
to feathers discarded –
life no more.

Wild eyes
stare through a plastic bag.

Later,
cold and naked,
he lies
on a market stall
long neck down
over the edge,
wings spread out
in final surrender.

Even this
is not enough.

Grandmother's Signature

Una Woods

Not a woman to shed tears easily
I saw her that day
in the shaded hall unobtrusively cry
It was over an old brown cow

Useless barren beast yielding
neither milk nor damn all else
I heard her curse it and it lumbering
aimlessly about the yard
dribbling and humping towards any doorway

But now as the men prodded and pushed
shoved the unwilling bulk into the lorry
as we stood a reluctant guard of honour
embarrassed by its predicament
its last humiliation

Through the window I saw Grandmother's face
contorted and wet
the pen limp in her hand

My Mother's House

Ruth Hooley

You, coming downstairs
with a mewing black cat in your wake,
coming to the door with wet hands
or into the room with a tray of porcelain cups.

The day you went away
curtains hung unopened, rooms
held their breath, stagnant without
you to open doors and windows to the light.

It grew too tall for you in the end;
cobwebs hanging from corners of neglect
reflected nothing of your bright
attentive ways to make us all important.

I lived there a while
each wall untouched,
in your room where fingers of firstlight
poked through holes in the blinds to lace my bed.

It wasn't the same. Your house
shuttered within the one fading over the fireplace.
Each time I wanted it
to be you in the mirror, without white hair.

Finding a way to house the past
I see you better, back to the light
And when you visit me
It will be always summer in a shady room –

I will not need to ask.

From
The Christmas Tree
Jennifer Johnston

*Constance has returned to her old family home and to the
memories within its walls. Flitting back and forth from the
past to the present, she seeks to make sense of her life in
the recent knowledge that she is terminally ill.*

The first time that I experienced the reality of physical
pain was when I was having the child. I had prepared
myself both mentally and physically for the experience; I
had read all the books, done all the exercises, learnt to
relax, attended clinics and lectures and film shows. I had
gone dutifully through the intelligent woman's guide to
childbirth. Pain is a myth. We had absorbed the words as
we lay on the floor practising our slow breathing and
then our fast breathing. You may at moments experience slight discomfort, we were promised as we exer-
cised our leg muscles; yet in the end of all, pain did exist.
A vast pattern of pain, like some formal dance, advancing and retreating slow turns, advance, bow, return.
Pause. Then the rhythm starting again beating in the pit
of your body, advance, retreat, turn slowly, turn, pause.
It didn't frighten me, even when the pauses became
inadequate for me to collect my equilibrium. I am frightened now. There is no rhythm now. I get no warning. It
is like being eaten by some animal that tears at me until
its hunger is temporarily satisfied and then it sleeps
uneasily until the hunger starts again. I stuff myself full
of Bill's pills and wash them down with whiskey and then
wait until my mind becomes so confused that I neither
understand nor feel anything. At those moments my
mother's face pushes itself before my eyes. Tiny hunted
face, burnt out eyes, wisps of hair lank on her pillow.
Not even a shadow of herself, rather some monstrous
caricature.

'What have you done to her?'

The panic in my voice echoed off the pale green walls of the passage in the nursing home. A table outside her door was covered with flowers. The room itself had been filled with roses, carnations, irises, azaleas, but their smell was drowned by the smell of disease and fear.

'Why the hell don't you leave her alone?'

'Ssssh, Constance. You're upset. Of course you are. It's such ages since you've seen her. You're just catching her on a bad day. Tomorrow she may be as right as rain. Perky as anything, chatting away. She goes up and down. You must understand that.'

Her finger and thumb dug into my elbow, demanding restraint.

'We must never give up hope, give up trying. Doctor Butterworth says she is responding very well to treatment.'

My heels squeaked on the polished floor as I ran.

An elderly woman in a flowery overall was cleaning the brass in the church. She rattled knobs and handles with a yellow duster. The cold air was filled with the smell of Brasso. I walked up to the front pew, pulled out a hassock and knelt down. Last Sunday's flowers still drooped on the altar. I racked my brains to think of a prayer. They could do with some of her flowers around here, I thought. She had had a prie Dieu in her room, with tiny carved feet and an old tapestry kneeler. She used to pray every night before she went to bed. Our Father which art in heaven, Hallowed be Thy name.

I had found her at it once when I had not been able to sleep and had wandered into her room in search of possible company. She hadn't moved when I opened the door. Her head was bent over her clasped hands and the light from the lamp beside her bed shone in the long hair which was hanging around her shoulders, like a young girl's hair. I loved her at that secret moment. I slipped out of the room without speaking.

Thy Kingdom come; Thy will be done on earth as it is in heaven. Thy will be done. Let Thy will be to take her now. As I speak. The lady with the brass polish moved

171

past me up to start work on the altar rail, and possibly keep an eye on me. I could see by her face that she thought home was the best place for prayer, except for the ordered hours on Sundays and Holy days.

Hear me. Mercifully hear me.

Of course I realise the irony that Bibi is at this moment probably in some church, saying Oh Lord please let her live. So where does that leave You, oh Lord?

I imagine she carries more clout than I do.

Nonetheless, I would be grateful, Lord, if You would let her depart in peace. Soon. Now.

For Thine is the Kingdom the Power and the Glory, for ever and ever. Amen.

I got up.

The polisher turned and looked at me.

'Nice day,' she whispered.

'Yes.' I whispered back.

I had always felt that after my mother's death I would find some kind of release, the awareness for the first time of an identity. It wasn't that we had been great friends or even communicated with each other in any important way. On the contrary I had always seemed to be a source of great irritation to her, a curious disappointment. The fact that I had been born the wrong sex had been the first major setback, from which our relationship never really recovered.

I felt angered as I walked among the cold tombstones, not only about the circumstances of her death but also that I still felt the same confusion inside myself that I always had. It was then in the flurry of windblown snow that the first thoughts came to me that I should have a child. I pushed the idea away. There in the landscape it seemed grotesque. I went home with Father and Bibi to hand round drinks and plates of savouries to the family's mourning friends. That evening, slightly drunk and still wearing my black coat I boarded the B and I boat and went back to London.

A Death in the Family

Francine Cunningham

We hadn't told a sinner,
but she read
tea-leaves
and said she'd leave
the Fairisle

in a dog's dinner.

She kept Saint Anthony's prayer
in her underwear
against the surgeon's scar,
but one day, it flushed
away.

In the end, spoon-fed,
communion could not be swallowed,
famished Heaven,
jaundiced, hallowed,
hunger strikes.

Willed, but unwilled,
the last contorted rattle
sank with grateful gravity,
a candle feverishly forced
to a limp hand

ring-a-ring-a-rosary.

Weighted stench of death
begun in life.
A delicate red-legged cell
minced across the carpet
leaving its Hell,
surreptitiously.

Sunday Visit

Mary Twomey

There she sits
Unchanged
In the same
Precise museum arrangement
Of meal chest and butter churn
Comfortless straight-backed chairs
Laid out on the flagged floor.

A smelly oil lamp
Hallows the Sacred Heart
Smoky range fire is a
Tabernacle lamp
Signal
That she is at home today.

Her humped back
Is upturned towards
The eternal twilight window
Shrivelled apple face
Turned from the light
So that I or anybody
May not guess
She is alive today.

I sit
On a begrudged chair
Forcing dry bone words
I think
Of the proud girl
I've heard about
Long brushed hair
Thick velvet dresses
Riding high in a pony trap
When all around her
Went on foot.

She asks indifferently now

About caring relatives
Then folds her hands and face
And turns her head away
The audience is over
She bids me set the chair
Just there
And drags herself to the door
Before I've even stood
And then
But not always
She smiles.

Bone China and Old Lace

Elizabeth Miller

We, as schoolgirls, laughed at them behind our hands,
Their backs stiff, straight; their faces prim.
Spinsters. Dry as dust. We imagined
Them, if we thought of them at all,
Contented in their ordered lives,
Their tidy houses, behind starched curtains,
And felt contempt, knowing we wanted more.
We did not know how many quiet mouthings screened
Silent screams echoing from empty walls,
How many gowns of crusted lace
Hid shells the moth consumed
As the fires went out.
Giggling, we did not understand
How bitter was the brew
They sipped from flowered china cups
Brittle as bone.

Babushka*

Bernadette Ross

They are in layers and dark folds
and their skin is beaten by history.
REMNANTS of '1917'.
But it's the way they wear their scarves
that makes me want to call them
Peasants of the Eighties,
still carrying their bundles like
there's no tomorrow.

* 'Babushka' is an old Russian word for 'grandmother'.

June 23rd

Jan Kennedy

Martha closed the door behind her, checked it was secure, and walked briskly up the hill towards the shops.
Today was Tuesday and pension day, so Martha had, as
she had every Tuesday for the past 15 years, explained
slowly and patiently to mother and father that she would
be back a little later than usual. And that she would, of
course, be home in time to ensure they had their med-
icine before lunch. Not that she had much faith in these
famous medicines her parents took on waking, before
eating, after meals, before sleeping, and at several other
points during the day. But if they felt they were doing
some good, then Martha supposed that was the main
thing. Which reminded her – Martha stopped and took
out a small notebook, 'A Present from Corfu' was written in slanted golden print across the front. It was really
an address book but, as Martha didn't write to many
people nowadays, she hadn't any trouble remembering
the addresses. Still, it had been kind of Edwina to send
her the book and, rather than waste it, she used the small
pages for keeping lists, of books to order in the library,
programmes to watch on television (time permitting),
and, the most important, THINGS TO BE DONE BY
JUNE 23rd. Martha quickly added 'Repeat prescriptions' to this already lengthy list and popped the book and
pen back into her handbag. 'Only two more days' Martha thought to herself, and smiled.

Outside the post office Martha met Doctor Brown,
the family's recently retired G.P.

'Another lovely day, Martha. How are your parents
keeping?'

'Just the same, you know,' she replied.

'They're so lucky to have you at home Martha, not
many have such good daughters. Send them my best
regards. All the best now. Cheerio.'

Martha watched Dr. Brown's tall figure move through the early morning shoppers, stopping here and there to exchange a greeting with former patients and acquaintances. 'Yes,' she thought to herself, 'I suppose *I have* been a good daughter. But what else could I have done when father had the stroke so soon after mother's accident? Edwina was already in England at the time and really couldn't have been expected to come home, what with her job and, of course, the engagement.' Martha shook herself. 'Now thinking about that isn't going to get the shopping done,' and, briskly, she turned and went into the post office.

Because Edwina would find it hard (she always did) to settle into the routine, Martha usually left a collection of lists and notes on the kitchen table for her to consult. Since she was to arrive on Thursday afternoon and Martha would be leaving almost immediately, she decided to order the fish now so Edwina only had to pop into Maguire's to collect it. No fuss, no possibility of the wrong sort of fish (father was *so* particular) or, even worse, no chance of the fish being sold out as Edwina did tend to leave the shopping till a little late in the day.

'Right you are now, Miss Boyle, I'll have it ready for your sister to collect on Friday. It's been a while since we've seen her, last year wasn't it? About this time? Nice for your parents to have her over to stay for a bit.'

Martha nodded and smiled. Mother and father would, of course, be very pleased to see her. Edwina was always so full of life, full of stories and laughter. A real tonic. 'Not as dull a companion as I am,' she thought. But then it's easier to have plenty to say if you're only here for two weeks. Easy to have plenty of stories when you have an office full of people to talk to every day, a husband who adores you and a social life that never seems to slow down. 'Damn,' Martha said to herself, 'that's twice in one day. I really must not go over all that again. Edwina was so young when it all happened. How could I expect an energetic 20-year-old with such talent to give it all up and come home to look after mother and father? And what would Michael, a Londoner, have

179

done over here with the possibility of work so slight?'
But the fact was that Martha, a not quite so energetic
30-year-old, had been expected to give up her job and
rather cosy little flat in Coleraine to care for the invalids.
Doctor Brown said there was nothing else for it. Father
said he would never go into a Home while there was a
daughter here in the North to look after him. Mother
just fixed Martha with a look that she would never
forget. So, of course, she came home. And, for the most
part, it wasn't too bad. She always had the June holiday
to think about. Every year Edwina came to stay for two
weeks in June to allow Martha to get away to the seaside.
Mother always believed in the value of sea air, and she
was right. Greystones. She could smell the sea already,
hear the waves rolling over the pebbled beach, feel the
sea breeze in her hair and picture the tall cross on the
Head at Bray, watching over the sea and jagged rocks
below. 'Only two more days,' thought Martha, and
smiled.

Martha woke early on Thursday morning. Although tired from yesterday's efforts to leave everything
in the house well organised for Edwina, she hadn't slept
a great deal. 'Imagine a woman of my age being as
excited as any 10-year-old child about two weeks by the
sea,' Martha laughed to herself, but quietly, for fear of
waking mother who slept in the other bed. She had had a
good night, only two trips, with Martha's help, to the
commode which was a permanent fixture in the small
bedroom. Martha allowed herself the luxury of a rather
contented stretch in bed before getting up to attend to
the usual morning routine of helping father out of bed,
taking him to the toilet, bathing him and getting him
settled in his wheelchair, before repeating the exercise
with mother. This morning, she anticipated, could be
problematic. While mother and father were, of course,
delighted that Edwina was coming today, they always
got a bit tight-lipped and sulky with Martha whom they
considered 'a deserter' for these annual two weeks. Because of this pre-departure moodiness, she and Edwina
merely exchanged greetings on Edwina's arrival, leaving

180

Martha's return, the day before the fortnight was over, for a family tea-party and general exchange of news and gossip. Today was no exception and Martha, despite her resolution to remain patient, found herself feeling very irritable when she had to repeat, for at least the sixth time, that she had left a note (with all the other notes and lists) for Edwina, explaining that father no longer required the yellow pill at 4.00 pm, but instead took a green pill at 6.00 pm, after he had finished his tea. 'Only a few more hours,' she thought with relief.

The rattle of the letterbox startled Martha. Very few letters came to the household and it was too early for the end-of-the-month bills to arrive. Martha looked at the peach-coloured envelope for a long time. It was undoubtedly Edwina's untidy handwriting, but what on earth would Edwina be writing about since she was due here, in person, in only a few hours?

She re-read the single sheet of paper, slowly put it back in the envelope and stood looking out of the window at father's rose-bed she had weeded so carefully earlier this week. Father was very precise about his rose-bed and had supervised her closely from the sitting-room window while she had pricked out every trace of grass or dandelion from the rich dark soil. Martha looked at her suitcase, neatly packed and ready by the door, then at the stiff envelope in her hand.

'I know I should have let you know earlier, should at least have phoned to say I wasn't coming. Cowardly of me perhaps, but I know you will understand. I just cannot go on with this charade of the dutiful daughter. I can't go on pretending to enjoy my stay at home. I come back here to Michael, at the end of the fortnight, exhausted. He feels the strain is too much for me and I really cannot be expected to go on doing it. I know you'll understand, Martha, and think of some excuse for me.

Your loving sister,
Edwina.'

She stood for a moment longer, put the envelope with its matching single sheet of paper into her pocket, then went to the kitchen where mother and father were

181

waiting for Martha to help them with their lunch.

'What *have* you been doing, Martha? Your mother is starving.'

'Sorry, father, I had to answer the telephone. It was Edwina. Her hired car has had a puncture so she'll be a little later than usual. She knew I had to catch the 3.30 bus to Dublin so suggested I should go on ahead to the bus depot on foot. She's outside Larne now so should be here by four at the latest. Now mother, let's get the soup down. Easy now or you'll choke.'

The dishes washed, best summer coat over her arm, Martha closed the door behind her, checked it was secure, and walked briskly up the hill.

Mistaken Stratagem

Elizabeth Miller

My only vein of ore now almost mined,
The prospect's bleak.
I have no natural riches, no fine flocks,
A hard, inclement climate, barren rocks,
The snow-line low, below it straggling trees,
Few woods of use in carpentry, few streams
For power. A poor country indeed,
Until I made discovery of my one resource
Far underground, in un-illumined dark
A sheen of metal, unpromising, thin at first,
Then offering ever richer stores.
Drunk with joy I set to work.
Long hours, then years, were spent in my dark task,
Always alone, this sort of mining needs no other hand
And I was jealous of possession and sought to keep it.
Exhaustion creeps upon me, there is little left
Of time or metal now, both mine and miner
Near worked-out.
My economic strategy was poor,
I should have made some use
Of all that precious metal, polished it
For adornment or for currency
Not hoarded it away, in closed accounts.

Acknowledgements

Acknowledgements are due to the following:

Arlen House, who first published 'The Wall-Reader' by Fiona Barr as first prizewinner of the Maxwell House Women's Short Story Competition in 1979; *The Belfast Review*, who first published 'All I Ask' and 'One Autumn' by Maura Johnston, and 'Woman Alone' by Ruth Hooley; BBC Radio Ulster, who first broadcast *Myself* by Dorothy Gharbaoui; *Caret*, who first published 'The Chain' by Anne Tannahill; *Envoi*, who first published 'Chivalry' by Anne Strain; *Fortnight*, who first published 'Nursery Rhyme' by Ruth Hooley; Hamish Hamilton, who first published *The Christmas Tree* by Jennifer Johnston; Hodder and Stoughton, who first published *A Furnished Room* by Janet McNeill; The *Irish Press*, who first published 'The Cage' by Frances McEnaney, 'The Countrywoman' by Una Woods and 'Under Control' by Mary Beckett in their New Irish Writing section; *The Literary Review*, who first published 'Five Notes After a Visit' by Anne Devlin (it has also been broadcast on BBC Radio Three and is to be published by Faber and Faber in a collection of stories by the author in 1986); RTE Radio, who first broadcast 'The Reprisal' by Jill McKenna; *Women's News*, who first published 'Rape' by Christine Hammond.

Notes on the Contributors

Fiona Barr

Born in Derry in 1952. Apart from 'The Wall-Reader' she has had numerous stories and articles published and broadcast on Radio Four. The short story 'Sisters', first published in the collection of the same title by Blackstaff Press, is being adapted as a play for BBC. She is currently television critic for the *Irish News*, mother of four and very tired.

Mary Beckett

Born in 1926 in Belfast. Taught in Ardoyne for ten years. Married in 1956 and went to live in Dublin. Reared five children. In the fifties she had stories published in *The Bell, New Irish Writing, Threshold* and broadcast on BBC radio. In 1980 Poolbeg Press brought out a collection of her stories, called *A Belfast Woman*. Now out of print.

Evelyn Berman

Born in Dungannon. An infant teacher for twelve years, she now lives in Belfast where she is no longer a mere 'redundant mother' but works part-time in a women's centre, writes, studies and enjoys her grandchildren.

Shirly Bork

Trained as a designer and works freelance as a set designer in the theatre. Has always written and runs Queen's extra-mural Writers' Club. Has had poems, stories and articles published and broadcast on BBC's *Woman's Hour, Morning Story, Bazaar, Northern Drift* and *Pen to Paper*. Married with five children.

Geraldine Bradley

Born in Bessbrook, county Armagh. Active in the women's rights movement and an ardent mountaineer. Wrote 'Pictures' when she was sixteen. Directed a production of her first play, *A Few Changes Around Here*, for the Belfast Festival of Women in the Arts in 1984 while studying at the Ulster University.

Francine Cunningham

Born in Strabane in 1964. Presently studying English and Philosophy at Queen's University Belfast. Poems published in *Gown* Literary Supplement.

Anne Devlin

Born in Belfast in 1951. Her short story, 'Passages', for which she won the Hennessy Literary Award in 1982, was adapted for television as *A Woman Calling* in April 1984. Stories published by Faber and the *Literary Review*. A television version of her radio play, *The Long March*, was shown on Play for Today in 1984. She won the 1984 Samuel Beckett Award for Television Drama. Now lives in Birmingham and has one son.

Polly Devlin
Born in county Tyrone. Now living and writing in England. *All of Us There*, a testimony of what it was like to grow up in N. Ireland, has gone into Pan paperback. Her collection of short stories, *The Far Side of the Lough*, was published by Gollancz in 1985. 'Dora' is a chapter from a novel to be published by Chatto & Windus.

Dorothy Gharbaoui
Born and educated in Belfast. Taught English, then married and became a full-time writer while raising a family. Over 20 radio plays and varied freelance journalism for local and national journals. Nowadays works in public relations, head of a one-parent family.

Ann W. Gleave
Writer, anarchist, feminist, vegan. Mad about Ry Cooder. Originally a Lancastrian, was uprooted and reached 'home base', as she puts it, in Ireland. Lives in Belfast. Has written poems, reviews, articles, news features (even horroscopes!), countless letters. Active supporter of animal rights. Presently unemployed.

Christine Hammond
Born in Lisburn in 1958. Currently working as an administrative assistant and studying part-time for a degree at Queen's University. Published in *Gown* Literary Supplement and *Women's News*.

Ruth Hooley
Born in Belfast where she still lives with her daughter. Father worked in the shipyard, mother taught art. Graduated from Queen's University in 1976. Poems, articles, reviews published in many journals. Currently employed to produce publications for the Northern Ireland Women's Rights Movement.

Anne Jago
Married with three children. Presented with the Creative Writing Trophy at St Louise's Adult Community School where she is studying for A levels. Has been writing poetry for many years and has had several published. Member of the Ulster Worker Writers' Group.

Jennifer Johnston
Born in Dublin, 1930. Started writing about 1966. Her novels include *The Captains and the Kings, How Many Miles to Babylon?, Shadows on Our Skin, The Christmas Tree*, and her most recent one, *The Stationmaster*. She now lives in Derry. The youngest of her four children has just gone to university.

Maura Johnston
Born in 1946 in South Derry. Graduated from Queen's University in 1967, married in 1968 and lived in Africa until 1975. Returned to Moneymore where she teaches and looks after her

three children. Poems published in *Poetry Ireland Review,
Belfast Review* and the *Ulster Tatler*.

Marie Jones

Founder-member of Charabanc Theatre Company which is
made up mostly of women and committed to community-based
drama. The highly successful *Lay Up Your Ends*, written
jointly by Charabanc and playwright Martin Lynch, was their
first play. It toured many places including Moscow. Charabanc
have since written and performed various sketches and two
more plays: *Oul' Delf and False Teeth* and *Now You're Talkin'*.
Marie is the main scriptwriter for the group.

Eileen Kelly

Born in Belfast in the Lower Falls. Left school at fifteen.
Always a keen reader. Married with five children and eight
grandchildren. Has had more opportunity to write in recent
years. 'Still Life' is her first poem to be published.

Jan Kennedy

Born in Ballymoney in 1955. Became interested in writing
while a student in England. Married, she now lives and works
in Derry. 'June 23rd' is her first story to be published.

Frances McEnaney

Born in Belfast, 1916. Domestic Science teacher for a short
time but the ballet dancer still calls to be let out. A very late
arrival to the literary scene. 'The Cage' came third in the *Irish
Times* short story competition and was subsequently published
in *New Irish Writing*. Also broadcast on RTE radio, as well as
several others since. BBC radio have broadcast her stories and
her first radio play, so far.

Mary McGowan

Born in Derry, 1942. Married with six children whose ages
range from 6 to 20. Has been writing bits and pieces since
childhood but never considered trying to get anything published before.

Medbh McGuckian

Born in Belfast, 1950. Graduated from Queen's University and
is presently teaching, writing and rearing three sons. Winner of
the National Poetry Award in 1979. Books published: *Single
Ladies* (Interim Press, 1980); *Portrait of Joanna* (Ulsterman
Publications, 1980); a contributor in *Trio* (Blackstaff Press,
1981); *The Flowermaster* (OUP, 1982); *Venus and the Rain*
(OUP, 1984).

Jill McKenna

Born in Belfast. Educated at Lurgan College. Married with a
seven-year-old son. Started writing fiction five years ago. Has
had a number of short stories published and one broadcast on
RTE radio.

Blanaid McKinney

Born in 1961 in county Fermanagh. Graduated in Political

187

Science from Queen's University and currently engaged in research into feminism and marxism, with particular interest in women and the Belfast linen industry. Poems have appeared in *Fortnight, Belfast Review, Irish Press* and the London *Literary Review*.

Janet McNeill
Born in Dublin in 1907, the daughter of a minister. After graduating from St Andrew's University she returned to Ireland to work in the *Belfast Telegraph*. She married and lived in Lisburn while her four children were growing up. Began writing plays for radio and then went on to write ten novels, articles, a couple of opera librettos and many children's books. Some of her work has been translated into various languages, including Japanese, and several have been published in the United States. Her novel, *The Maiden Dinosaur*, was reissued last year by Arlen House and Blackstaff Press. Now a widow, she lives in Bristol.

Kate Madden
Born and living in Belfast with her three children. Always wrote bits and pieces throughout her life as a means of coming to terms with things. Never dreamed of publishing anything.

Stella Mahon
Born in Belfast in 1945 where she has lived for thirty of her forty years. Works for the Open University and took an Honours degree with them as well, majoring in History. She has had short stories published by Blackstaff Press in *Sisters*, and has contributed to two books on women's issues published by Arlen House. One of her stories was read on BBC Radio Four some years ago. Currently working on her first novel. Lives with a friend, four cats and her teenage daughter.

Patricia Mallon
A mature student, now teaching English in St Louise's Comprehensive College. Only started writing recently and says she is motivated to continue because of the pleasure it gives her.

Sandra Marshall
Born and still lives in Belfast. Started writing verse quite recently, mostly to be read out loud for the crack. 'The Girls in the Big Picture' is her first piece to be published.

Elizabeth Miller
Born 1937 in Belfast. Spent the Blitz years moving from one relative to another but returned to Belfast in 1945 and has left it since only for holidays. Says Queen's University was a good place to be in the late fifties. Eventually lectured in Educational Psychology at Stranmillis College until early retirement through ill health. Started writing stories early on, poems came later, with some published.

Frances Molloy
Born in county Derry, 1947. Her first novel, *No Mate for the*

Magpie, was published by Virago Press in 1985. Her short stories have appeared in various local magazines around Lancaster where she now lives with her husband and two children.

Sheila Mulvenna
Born in Belfast. Mother of four. Mainly interested in writing short stories for children and poetry. Now studying Literature and Psychology.

Brenda Murphy
Born in Belfast in 1954. Now lives in Downpatrick. Has been writing since she was seventeen. Most recently published in *No Place for Dogs*, by the residents of Divis Flats.

Anne Noble
Born in Dublin. Married an Ulsterman and came to live in the north. Has three children and three grandchildren. Was always interested in writing and also paints. Member of the Ulster Women Artists and the Royal Ulster Academy Association.

Christina Reid
Born in Belfast where she now lives with her three daughters. She won the UTV Drama Award in 1980 with her play, *Did You Hear the One About the Irishman? Tea in a China Cup* was runner-up in the *Irish Times*/Dublin Theatre Festival Competition for plays by women in 1982. It has subsequently been produced in London, Scotland and N. Ireland. She has recently completed two new plays and has had short stories published and broadcast on radio.

Geraldine Reid
Born and raised in Belfast. Always interested in writing, she is a member of the Ulster Worker Writers' Group.

Anne-Marie Reilly
Born in Belfast in the fifties. Now living in Strangford where she is a teacher. Hadn't seriously written before joining a writing group.

Delia Rimington
Born in Cheshire. Married, with one daughter in America. Is a craft worker and painter, now settled in N. Ireland.

Bernadette Ross
Born in Belfast, 1960. Studying German, Russian and Swedish at Queen's University. Has travelled widely, most recently in the USSR. Plays the viola. Doesn't write when she is happy.

Carol Scanlon
Born in Glengormley, outside Belfast, in 1956. Trained as a teacher of Drama and English at Stranmillis College. An actress in Charabanc Theatre Company since it formed in 1983. Charabanc are curently working on ideas for a television situation comedy and have plans for a film.

Janet Shepperson
Brought up in Scotland. Studied English at Aberdeen Uni-

versity and taught several years in Northern Ireland where she now lives. Hoping to write a novel.

Laura Shier

Grew up in Cork. Studied French and English at Trinity College, Dublin. Taught many years in Friends' School, Lisburn, where she met and married a teacher of mathematics. Has two grown-up sons. Exhibits paintings with the Royal Ulster Academy Association and the Ulster Women Artists.

Anne Strain

Born in Garvagh, county Derry, in 1938. Has lived in Kent since 1970 with her husband and two daughters. Poems published in various journals including *Aquarius, Envoi, Outposts, Poetry South East 6* and *Quarto*. GB representative of the Peace People. Involved in Sevenoaks Peace Forum, UNA and Amnesty International.

Anne Tannahill

Born in Belfast, 1942 (maiden name Bell). Left school at sixteen, worked in NI Civil Service until dismissed on marriage in 1962. (So-called 'marriage ban' excluded married women from employment in Service.) Worked in NI Special Care Service, leaving to have (only) child in 1965. Returned to education through evening classes and graduated from Queen's University with BA and MA in English. Taught for two years, then entered publishing. Currently a director of The Blackstaff Press in Belfast.

Mary Twomey

Born in Downpatrick where she still lives and teaches. 'Exile' is for Eoin, her mentally handicapped son. Has written poetry for about ten years. Never previously published.

Una Woods

Born and reared in Belfast. Worked for some years in London before marrying and moving to Dublin for six years. Returned to Belfast where she is now raising her two children. Has had several short stories published. Her first collection, *The Dark Hole Days*, was published by Blackstaff Press last year.